PREPOSITIONS

about	in
above	inside
across	into
after	near
against	of
along	off
around	on
at	out
before	outside
behind	over
below	past
beneath	through
beside	throughout
between	to
by	toward
down	under
during	until
except	up
for	with
from	without

Name_____   **PREPOSITIONS**

Date_____

A. Directions: Write the preposition with the opposite meaning.

1. up - down

2. in - out

3. above - below

4. over - under

5. inside - outside

6. with - without   9/15

7. before - after

8. on - off

9. to - from

B. Directions: Unscramble the following prepositions.

1. nulit - until

2. otaub - about

3. enar - near

4. gloan - along   9/16

5. weeetbn - betwee

6. drungi - during

7. hendbi - behind

8. saitgan - against

9. rossac - across

2

Name_____   **PREPOSITIONS**

Date_____

(A) Directions: Write the prepositions that begin with **a**:

1. about   4. after   7. around
2. above   5. against   8. at
3. across   6. along

(B) Directions: Write the prepositions that begin with **b**:

1. before   4. beneath   7. by
2. behind   5. beside
3. below   6. between

(C). Directions: Write the prepositions that begin with **d**:

1. down   2. during

D. Directions: Write the prepositions that begin with **o**:

1. Of   3. On   5. outside
2. Off   4. Out   6. over

E. Directions: Write the prepositions that begin with **t**:

1. Through   3. to
2. throughout   4. Toward

F. Directions: Write the prepositions that begin with **u**:

1. Under   2. Until   3. Up

		FREE		

4

Name_____   **PREPOSITIONS**

Date_____

A. Directions: Write the prepositions that have only two letters:

1. _to_   3. _up_   5. _by_   7. _of_

2. _in_   4. _at_   6. _on_

B. Directions: Write the prepositions that have three letters:

1. _out_   2. _off_   3. _for_

C. Directions: Write the prepositions that have four letters:

1. _down_   3. _from_   5. _into_   7. _near_

2. _with_   4. _over_   6. _past_

D. Directions: Write the prepositions that have five letters:

1. _under_   3. _until_   5. _along_   7. _below_

2. _after_   4. _about_   6. _above_

E. Directions: Write the prepositions that have six letters:

1. _before_   4. _inside_   7. _during_

2. _beside_   5. _across_   8. _behind_

3. _except_   6. _toward_   9. _around_

F. Directions: Write the prepositions that have seven letters:

1. _through_   3. _between_   5. _without_

2. _without_   4. _except_   6. _beneath_

5

Name_____   **PREPOSITIONS**

Date_____

A. Directions: Prepositions add meaning to a sentence.   Draw a desk. On the lines
                 at the bottom of this page, write sentences explaining how a desk can
                 be used. Be sure to use a preposition in each sentence.

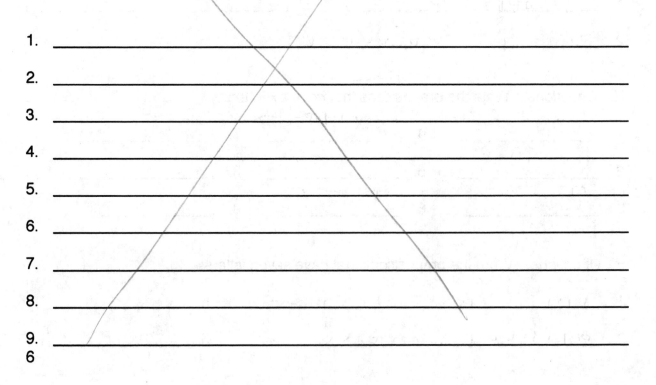

Examples: You can put something **into** a desk.

             A calculator may be **inside** a desk.

1. _____

2. _____

3. _____

4. _____

5. _____

6. _____

7. _____

8. _____

9. _____

Name_____   **PREPOSITIONS**

Date_____

9/23

A. Directions: Circle any preposition(s) in the following sentences.

1. A gray kitten drank milk from a small dish.

2. This package is for Mrs. Smith.

3. Don't leave without me.

4. That puppy with short ears is cute.

5. The next game starts at ten o'clock.

6. Put the ice cream into the freezer, please.

7. The soup of the day was potato.

8. Come and sit by me.

9. We walked around the park.

10. A sign hangs over their door.

11. I'll be ready in a minute.

12. They sat under an oak tree for a picnic.

13. Let's go to the store after breakfast.

14. A child ran down the steps and through the hallway.

15. She jumped off the swing and fell on the ground.

16. All desserts except peach pie had been sold.

17. During the summer months, the Jones family may go to Canada.

18. His favorite spot in the winter is outside his bedroom window.

19. Mayor Dalton leaves for his office before dawn.

20. Birds visit their feeder throughout the fall.

Name_____   **PREPOSITIONS**

Date_____

A.   Directions: Circle any preposition(s) in the following sentences.

1.   A book about snakes is beside the lizard one.

2.   Several dishes inside the old cupboard were covered with dust.

3.   Marco lives in the country near a wide brook.

4.   A shovel is leaning against the barn below the hayloft window.

5.   We walked beneath many poplar trees along the narrow lane.

6.   Place your bicycle between the two houses until this evening.

7.   The group rode horses up a long trail past an old mine.

8.   The lady across the street keeps a broom behind her front door.

9.   Toward the end of the day, six boys played basketball at the park.

10.   A fisherman rushed out the door and threw his line into the stream.

11.   During the hurricane, everyone went inside the large building for shelter.

12.   Throughout the race, the car drivers had stayed on course.

13.   Mrs. Sung traveled to Orlando without her luggage.

14.   Before the show, we walked around the theater.

15.   Everyone except Paco jumped off the diving board.

16.   Several elderly people sat by the street light near a pond.

17.   We waited beside the road after the parade.

18.   Before Christmas, gifts were placed beneath a large pine tree.

19.   Lina and Kana walked through the courthouse door and turned to the left.

20.   The sun sinks behind those mountains at the end of each day.

8

Name_____   **PREPOSITIONS**

Date_____

A **prepositional phrase** is a **group of words** that **begins with a preposition**.
A prepositional phrase ends with a noun (usually something you can see) or a
pronoun (such as *him*, *her*, *them*, *us*, or *me*).

Example: (down) the steps

(with) a huge umbrella

(after) lunch

(between) us

When you see a prepositional phrase in a sentence, cross it out like this: ~~between us~~
If two are side by side, lift your pencil and mark two separate lines: ~~with me~~ ~~for lunch~~

🍓🍓🍓🍓🍓🍓🍓🍓🍓🍓🍓🍓🍓🍓🍓🍓🍓🍓🍓🍓🍓🍓🍓🍓🍓🍓🍓🍓🍓🍓🍓🍓

A.   Directions: Add a word or words to each preposition to form a prepositional
                   phrase:

1. <u>under</u> the table _____

2. <u>inside</u> the cat _____

3. <u>for</u> the face _____

4. <u>across</u> the foot _____

5. <u>in</u> my computer _____

6. <u>during</u> my war _____

B.   Directions: Cross out any prepositional phrase(s) in the following sentences.

1. The mop is ~~in the closet.~~

2. I went ~~to the store.~~

3. Sit ~~by me.~~

9

Name_____ **PREPOSITIONS**

Date_____

A. Directions: Cross out any prepositional phrase(s) in the following sentences.

Remember: **A prepositional phrase begins with a preposition and ends with a noun (usually something you can see) or a pronoun (such as *me*, *him*, *her*, *us*, or *them*).**

1. We bought hot dogs for the picnic.

2. Their uncle lives in Oregon.

3. Our car is parked past that alley.

4. A tourist walked over the old bridge.

5. The coach walked quickly toward us.

6. Mrs. Martin always runs before breakfast.

7. Their cat sleeps under an old chair.

8. The father put bread into a toaster.

9. Several ladies picked berries along the road.

10. Sue's favorite doll has a white hat with blue ribbons.

11. Several balloons were hung near the front door.

12. We cannot leave without our swimming suits.

13. Outside the city, Bill's family has a small cottage.

14. The workers leaned their shovels against the wall.

15. The letter from James is on the counter.

16. A fountain is located in the middle of the park.

17. This shirt was given to me by my aunt.

18. The children raced down several steps and rushed into the yard.
10

The word (noun or pronoun) that ends a prepositional phrase is called the object of the preposition.

O.P.

Example: Put the groceries into the cupboard.

🍓🍓🍓🍓🍓🍓🍓🍓🍓🍓🍓🍓🍓🍓🍓🍓🍓🍓🍓🍓🍓🍓🍓🍓🍓🍓🍓🍓🍓🍓🍓🍓🍓

Directions: Cross out the prepositional phrase in each sentence.   Label the object of
the preposition - **O.P.**

1.   He rode around the block.

2.   Sit by the door.

3.   A robin flew into its nest.

4.   Len fell over his bike.

5.   Come with me.

6.   The host talked to the audience.

7.   A worker threw garbage into the truck.

8.   Their aunt plays tennis at a club.

9.   The cherry pickers ate lunch under a tree.

10.   A corsage of pink roses was delivered.

11.   Wilma made a salad with frozen grapes.

12.   A taxi driver ran over a curb.

13.   This television show is about Hawaii.

14.   A gymnast climbed up a rope.

15.   His sandals are made of leather.

A prepositional phrase will not be the subject or verb of a sentence.*

SUBJECTS:

Crossing out prepositional phrases will help you to find the subject of a sentence.

      Example: In the pond, several fish swam near the surface.

      ~~In the pond~~, several fish swam ~~near the surface~~.

      Pond can't be the subject.   Why?   *Pond* is in a prepositional phrase.

Remember: The subject will not be found in a prepositional phrase. When you cross out the prepositional phrase, it's like pretending that those words have disappeared from the page.

To find the subject, look at the remaining words. Read them. Then, ask yourself **who** or **what** the sentence is about.

      Example: several fish swam

We are talking about fish; *fish* is the subject. Place one straight line under fish.

      Example: several <u>fish</u> swam

VERBS:

To find the verb, decide **what happened** (or **is happening**) or **what "is"** in the sentence. **The verb will never be in a prepositional phrase.**

      Oral reading: several fish swam

Repeat your subject, *fish*, and ask yourself, "What did the fish do?" The fish *swam*. Swam is the verb. Place double underlining under the verb: several <u>fish</u> <u>swam</u>.

          * This holds true 99% of the time.

Name_____   **PREPOSITIONS**

Date_____

Directions: Cross out the prepositional phrase in each sentence.   Underline the
               subject once and the verb twice.

                    Example: His dad lives near Mt. St. Helens.

1.   I left without money.

2.   The soap is below the sink.

3.   A bug flew up his sleeve.

4.   Many horses trotted along the wide path.

5.   Her cousin lives near a waterfall.

6.   Inside the box was a small quilt.

7.   The van beside the blue car is mine.

8.   Everyone except Sandy left early.

9.   A toddler crawled over his friend.

10.   A rabbit nibbled beneath a bush.

11.   We peeked under the bed.

12.   Shawn looked toward his laughing friends.

13.   The runner jumped over the hurdle.

14.   A ring fell to the floor.

15.   This letter is from their senator.

16.   My grandmother golfs with her friend.

17.   Chad shopped without his mother.

18.   She placed her towel between several sunbathers.

13

Name_____   **PREPOSITIONS**

Date_____

Directions: Cross out any prepositional phrase(s).   Underline the subject once and
the verb twice.

Example: His <u>sunglasses</u> <u><u>are</u></u> ~~beneath the sofa in the living room~~.

1.   Several <u>hens</u> <u><u>gathered</u></u> ~~by the shed~~.

2.   <u>Daisies</u> <u><u>grow</u></u> ~~outside their fence~~.

3.   A <u>seal</u> <u><u>swam</u></u> ~~toward the shore~~.

4.   <u>Marty</u> <u><u>fell</u></u> ~~off the bottom of the slide~~.

5.   A <u>dog</u> ~~without a leash~~ <u><u>trotted</u></u> ~~by them~~.

6.   Nightly, the <u>woman</u> <u><u>looks</u></u> ~~through her telescope~~.

7.   <u>They</u> <u><u>rushed</u></u> ~~across the yard after a rubber ball~~.

8.   <u>Mr. Carlson</u> <u><u>read</u></u> a book ~~about tigers to his son~~.

9.   <u>She</u> <u><u>rode</u></u> ~~around the corral on her favorite pinto~~.

10.   The <u>teenagers</u> <u><u>walked</u></u> ~~down the beach past the pier~~.

11.   A <u>dog</u> <u><u>darted</u></u> ~~across the street by the firehouse~~.

12.   <u>We</u> <u><u>walked</u></u> ~~between the aisles at the supermarket~~.

13.   The <u>drummer</u> <u><u>waited</u></u> ~~beside the road after the parade~~.

14.   The <u>sun</u> <u><u>sinks</u></u> ~~behind the mountains toward the end of the day~~.

15.   <u>They</u> <u><u>played</u></u> ~~against a team with blue and white jerseys~~.

14

Name_____

Date_____

Compound Subjects:

Sometimes a sentence will contain a compound subject.

Compound subject simply means that there will be **more than one** "who" or "what" in the sentence.   Compounds are usually joined with the conjunctions, *and* or *or*.

> Examples: His <u>father</u> and <u>mother</u> have arrived.
>
> <u>Janis</u>, <u>Kelly</u>, or <u>I</u> will be going, also.

Crossing out prepositional phrases will make it easier to find a compound subject.

> Example: The <u>lady</u> ~~with the red hat~~ and her <u>mother</u> are opera singers.

✿✿✿✿✿✿✿✿✿✿✿✿✿✿✿✿✿✿✿✿✿✿✿✿✿✿✿✿✿✿✿✿✿✿✿✿✿✿

Directions: Cross out any prepositional phrase(s).   Underline the subject once and the verb twice.

1.   His <u>dog</u> and <u>cat</u> <u>play</u> ~~in his backyard.~~

2.   Your <u>aunt</u> and <u>uncle</u> ~~from Texas~~ <u>are</u> here.

3.   A <u>pear</u> or <u>peach</u> <u>is</u> ~~in the refrigerator.~~

4.   The <u>mayor</u> and her <u>husband</u> <u>arrived</u> ~~at the dinner.~~

5.   <u>Dr. Shank</u> and his <u>nurse</u> <u>talked</u> ~~to the young patient.~~

6.   <u>Paper</u> and <u>pencils</u> <u>are</u> ~~inside the desk.~~

7.   <u>Mark</u>, <u>Kim</u>, or <u>Denise</u> <u>left</u> ~~for the park.~~

8.   A <u>candle</u>, three flower <u>pots</u>, a <u>vase</u>, and a red <u>box</u> <u>are</u> ~~on the shelf above the sink.~~

9.   A <u>bag</u> ~~of corn~~ and a <u>carton</u> ~~of fruit~~ <u>were</u> ~~under a wooden bench.~~

15

Name_____

Date_____

19/6

An imperative sentence gives a command. Usually, the subject is not written. The person knows that the message is intended for him.

Example: Pass the butter, please.

Notice that the sentence doesn't say, "You pass the butter, please." The *you* has been omitted because it's understood for whom the message was intended. The subject is written: (You) and said: "You understood."

Example: Follow this road.

(You) Follow this road.

Crossing out prepositional phrases will help:

Example: Sit by me for a few minutes.

(You) sit ~~by me for a few minutes~~.

🍓🍓🍓🍓🍓🍓🍓🍓🍓🍓🍓🍓🍓🍓🍓🍓🍓🍓🍓🍓🍓🍓🍓🍓🍓🍓🍓🍓🍓🍓🍓🍓🍓🍓🍓

Directions: Cross out any prepositional phrase(s). Underline the subject once and the verb twice.

(YOU) 1. Give this ~~to your brother~~.

(YOU) 2. Please look ~~into the camera~~.

(YOU) 3. Drive ~~by my friend's house~~.

(YOU) 4. Take the saw ~~to the tree trimmer~~.

(YOU) 5. Go ~~after lunch~~ ~~without me~~.

(YOU) 6. Sign ~~on the dotted line~~.

(YOU) 7. Please search ~~under the table~~ ~~for the lost keys~~.

16

Name_____

Date_____

Compound Objects of the Preposition:

Sometimes, a prepositional phrase will contain more than one object. This a called a compound object.

              O.P.   O.P.

Example: for Carol and me   Carol = object of the preposition

                            me = object of the preposition

Note: Look at the word after an object of the preposition. If *and* or *or* follows the noun or pronoun, check to see if there may be another noun or pronoun ending the prepositional phrase.

                      O.P.   O.P.

Example: He walked without his shoes or socks.

🍓🍓🍓🍓🍓🍓🍓🍓🍓🍓🍓🍓🍓🍓🍓🍓🍓🍓🍓🍓🍓🍓🍓🍓🍓🍓🍓🍓🍓🍓🍓🍓🍓🍓🍓

Directions: Cross out any prepositional phrase(s). Underline the subject once and the verb twice.

1. The shirt with dots and stripes is unusual.

2. (You) Go with your cousin or David.

3. The gift from Sam and Dora was large.

4. She eats her sandwiches without tomato or lettuce.

5. Their family reunion is in July or August.

6. (You) Take this with you for your lunch or dinner.

7. The road to Payson and Alpine has many bumps.

8. Your gardening tool is in the shed on the table or chair.

9. Throughout the fall and winter, we watch birds at that feeder.

10/8

Compound Verbs:

Sometimes a sentence contains more than one verb. This is called a compound verb. This means that the subject often "does" more than one item.

In order to determine a verb, first cross out any prepositional phrases. Then, find the subject of the sentence. Next, decide what the subject *is* (*was*) or *does* (*did*).

Examples: A sparrow sits on the fence and chirps.
What does the sparrow do? Two things: sits and chirps

The nurse took a bandage, opened it, and placed it on the man's arm.
What did the nurse do? Three things: took, opened, and placed

🍓🍓🍓🍓🍓🍓🍓🍓🍓🍓🍓🍓🍓🍓🍓🍓🍓🍓🍓🍓🍓🍓🍓🍓🍓🍓🍓🍓🍓🍓🍓🍓🍓🍓🍓

Directions: Cross out any prepositional phrase(s).   Underline the subject once and the verb twice.

1. A pretty receptionist smiled and handed a paper to a businesswoman.

2. After breakfast, Joe washed, rinsed, and dried the dirty dishes.

3. Harriet waved her hat, yelled, and stomped her foot in excitement.

4. The winner of the race dashed across the finish line and fell.

5. One of the boys clapped his hands and cheered happily.

6. Mr. Adams drives to a bus stop and travels by bus to his office.

7. A tiger has stripes, eats meat, and lives in Asia.

8. The delivery person knocked, waited for a few minutes, and left the package beside the door.

9. A deer with a fawn stepped into the meadow and stared toward us.

To plus a verb is called an infinitive.   *to be*

Examples: to go   to cry   to clean   to sing

Do not cross out infinitives. Place each infinitive in parenthesis (to sing). This will help you to remember not to mark it as a prepositional phrase.

Example: The librarian wants **(to read)** us a book.

Important note: *To* plus a noun or pronoun makes up a prepositional phrase.
Cross out any prepositional phrase.

to the store = prepositional phrase   to + store (noun)
to go = infinitive   to + go (verb)

In a sentence, cross out the prepositional phrase. Place parenthesis around the infinitive.

Example: Kyle wants (to go) to the store.

🍓🍓🍓🍓🍓🍓🍓🍓🍓🍓🍓🍓🍓🍓🍓🍓🍓🍓🍓🍓🍓🍓🍓🍓🍓🍓🍓🍓🍓🍓🍓🍓🍓🍓🍓🍓

Directions: Cross out any prepositional phrase(s).   Place parenthesis ( ) around each
infinitive. Underline the subject once and the verb twice.

1. Jacob loves (to read) about reptiles.

2. Heidi wanted (to be) an airplane pilot.

3. In the winter, Grandma loves (to ski.)

4. They promised (to write) soon.

5. Some tourists decided (to drive) by a marina.

6. Karen needs (to take) her backpack with her.

7. Several of the actors tried (to add) lines without the permission of the director.

19

Name_____

Date_____

A verb phrase is composed of one or more helping verbs plus a main verb. There are twenty-three helping verbs. These are also called auxiliary verbs.

do	has	may	can	could	is	were
does	have	might	shall	should	am	be
did	had	must	will	would	are	being
					was	been

The main verb is the last part of a verb phrase.

verb phrase	=	**helping verb(s)**	+	**main verb**
will learn	=	will	+	learn
could have brought	=	could have	+	brought

Directions: Cross out any prepositional phrase(s). Underline the subject once and the verb phrase twice.

1. I do love (to bake) during the afternoon.

2. A bug has bitten you on the arm.

3. You may come with us.

4. Isaac might have crawled under the table.

5. Mrs. Park should clean above her oven.

6. They are going through the tunnel.

7. I shall eat before the play.

8. The waitress must serve drinks before the food.

9. Everyone except Annie will be leaving by bus.

10. The bread had been broken into three chunks.

20

Date_____

Not (or n't) is never part of a verb phrase.   Not is an adverb.   Box not immediately.   This keeps you from underlining not as part of a verb phrase.

Example: Her father will **not** be going with them.

Remember: A verb phrase is composed of one or more helping verbs plus a main verb. The main verb is the last part of a verb phrase.

do	has	may	can	could	is	were
does	have	might	shall	should	am	be
did	had	must	will	would	are	being
					was	been

Directions: Cross out any prepositional phrase(s).   Box not. Underline the subject once and the verb phrase twice.

1. You must not go until Friday.

2. The small boy wouldn't play with his friends.

3. She must not have stayed inside the hotel.

4. That tall girl cannot play against the new team.

5. A few hikers could not reach the top of the hill.

6. One of the clerks would not leave after his shift.

7. John does not fish beside other people.

8. I shall not change my mind about the pool cover.

9. Hannah hasn't typed on a computer yet.

10. He may not have stopped at the store.

21

Name_____   **PREPOSITIONS**

Date_____

10/28

An interrogative sentence asks a question. To determine the subject and verb of an interrogative sentence, first change the sentence into a statement (declarative sentence).

> Example: Is your mother here?
>   Your <u>mother</u> <u>is</u> here.

Follow these steps:
1.   Delete any prepositional phrase(s).
2.   Find the subject (*who* or *what* the sentence is about).
3.   Determine the verb: what *is* [*was*] or *happens* [*happened*].
     Often, an interrogative sentence contains a verb phrase.

> verb phrase = helping verb(s) + main verb

> Example: interrogative: Has George been to Maine?
>   declarative: <u>George</u> <u>has been</u> ~~to Maine~~.

This list of helping verbs will help you to identify a verb phrase.

do	has	may	can	could	is	were
does	have	might	shall	should	am	be
did	had	must	will	would	are	being
					was	been

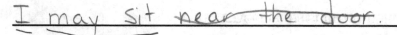

Directions: Rewrite the sentence, changing it into a statement. Then, cross out any prepositional phrase(s). Underline the subject once and the verb or verb phrase twice.

1.   Are we in the last row?

   <u>We</u> <u>are</u> ~~in the last row~~.

2.   May I sit near the door?

   <u>I</u> <u>may sit</u> ~~near the door~~.

3.   Will Toby go to camp?

   <u>Toby</u> <u>will go</u> ~~to camp~~.

A. **Preposition List:**

Directions: List the forty prepositions:

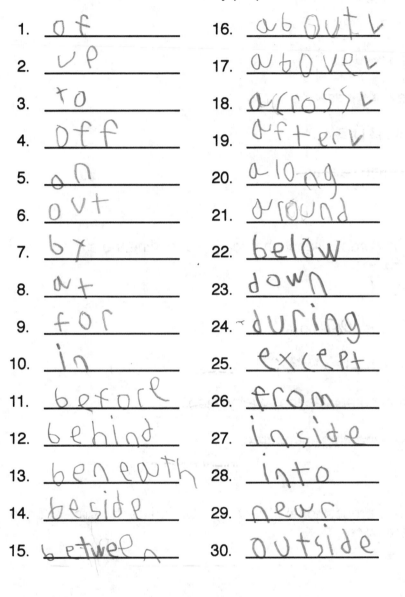

1. of
2. up
3. to
4. off
5. on
6. out
7. by
8. at
9. for
10. in
11. before
12. behind
13. beneath
14. beside
15. between

16. about
17. above
18. across
19. after
20. along
21. around
22. below
23. down
24. during
25. except
26. from
27. inside
28. into
29. near
30. outside

31. over
32. past
33. through
34. throughout
35. toward
36. under
37. untill
38. with
39. without
40. against

B. **Object of the Preposition:**

Directions: Cross out any prepositional phrase(s). Label the object of the preposition - O.P.

1. ~~During the winter,~~ rabbits nibble grass ~~above the snow.~~
   O.P.   O.P.

2. Peggy fished ~~across the stream~~ and sat ~~on a small rock~~ ~~for the entire day.~~
   O.P.   O.P.   O.P.

23

C. **Subject/Verb:**
    Directions: Cross out any prepositional phrase(s).   Underline the subject once
        and the verb twice.

1.   A ladybug crawled up his arm.

2.   They talked about their summer jobs.

3.   A green vine grows above her window.

4.   We leaned over the side of the bridge.

5.   A guide pointed toward a round building.

D. **Compound Subjects:**
    Directions: Cross out any prepositional phrase(s).   Underline the subject once
        and the verb twice.

1.   Lori and Jeff live by a river.

2.   Salt and pepper are behind the sugar bowl.

3.   Peter and his friend rode around the block.

4.   A guard and a customer chatted outside the jewelry shop.

5.   The cow and her calf stood beneath a shade tree.

E. **Imperative Sentences:**
    Directions: Cross out any prepositional phrase(s).   Underline the subject once
        and the verb twice.

1.   Please put this into the oven.

2.   Stay off the grass.

3.   Nail this shelf above the mirror.

4.   After dinner, please rinse the plates.

5.   Look in the garage for a tire pump.

F. **Compound Objects of the Prepositions:**
   Directions: Cross out any prepositional phrase(s).   Underline the subject once
                and the verb twice.

1. Warren has a snack of cookies and milk each afternoon.

2. We went to the amusement park with Frances, Susan, and Katie.

3. A birthday card from her aunt and uncle was on the kitchen counter.

4. That flower blooms only in the morning and evening.

5. A new deli serves cream cheese on bagels or rye toast.

G. **Compound Verbs:**
   Directions: Cross out any prepositional phrase(s).   Underline the subject once
                and the verb twice.

1. A shopper rushed toward the door but suddenly stopped.

2. All desserts except the pie are sugarless and taste wonderful.

3. Children played volleyball and ran around the playground during recess.

4. Her aunt lives near me and jogs by my house daily.

5. They went outside the roller-skating rink and talked for an hour.

H. **Verb Phrases:**
   Directions: Cross out any prepositional phrase(s).   Underline the subject once
                and the verb phrase twice.

1. I might have discovered a new path to the cave.

2. We had waited for the bus over an hour.

3. The coach had given her tips about sliding.

4. Senator Link is walking down the aisle with his daughter.

5. By sundown, we will be packing the car for our trip.   25

Name_____

Date_____

I. **Verb Phrases and <u>Not</u>:**

Directions: Cross out any prepositional phrase(s).   Underline the subject once and the verb phrase twice. Be sure to box *not*.

1.   I shall not speak with you about your behavior again.

2.   He hasn't applied for a college scholarship.

3.   The postman cannot deliver mail in the evening.

4.   Cynthia would not have forgotten to brush her teeth.

5.   They couldn't travel through Wales on their tour of Great Britain.

J. **Interrogative Sentences:**

Directions: Cross out any prepositional phrase(s).   Underline the subject once and the verb/verb phrase twice.

1.   Will you walk along the road with us?

2.   Do the Andersons go to church every Sunday?

3.   Are you using the computer from noon until two o'clock?

4.   Did Tina date during her sophomore year of college?

5.   Has the janitor fixed the door in the women's bathroom?

K.   **Prepositions:**

Directions: Cross out any prepositional phrase(s).   Underline the subject once and the verb/verb phrase twice.

1.   One of the gorillas held her baby under her arm.

2.   Jody hasn't been hired by the water company yet.

3.   At the meeting, the women spoke about their projects and planned a fashion show.

4.   During June, July, or August, they go to the shore to relax.

5.   Do Janet's dad and her grandfather fish in a trout stream near Caledonia Park?

26

Date_____

Direct Objects: Direct objects receive the action of the verb.

> Example: Kerry hit a ball.

> > What is the **object** Kerry hit?   Answer: ball
> > *Ball* is the direct object.

Sometimes, there will be a compound direct object.

> Example: The clerk sold shoes and sandals.

> > What are the **objects** the clerk sold?   Answer: shoes and sandals

To find a direct object:

1. Determine the subject of the sentence.

2. Find the verb. Ask what the subject is doing or did. **You will always have a verb that shows action in a sentence containing a direct object.**

3. Determine what object is being affected by the verb. Label the direct object- D.O.

🍓🍓🍓🍓🍓🍓🍓🍓🍓🍓🍓🍓🍓🍓🍓🍓🍓🍓🍓🍓🍓🍓🍓🍓🍓🍓🍓🍓🍓🍓🍓🍓🍓🍓🍓🍓🍓🍓🍓

Directions: Cross out any prepositional phrase(s).   Underline the subject once and the verb/verb phrase twice.   Label the direct object - D.O.

1. A maid at the hotel shook the rug.

2. Gordon placed a mat under the dog.

3. They read a book during the afternoon.

4. Harry flies kites on windy days.

5. Our brother cooked dinner for everyone.

6. A bellman carried our suitcases to our room.

7. Jill feeds her dog and cat before breakfast.

8. I bought a straw hat and a flowered dress today.

Name_____

Date_____

A. Directions: Cross out any prepositional phrase(s). Underline the subject once and the verb/verb phrase twice. Label any direct object - D.O.

1. We ate candy.

2. Aunt Freda threw the ball to me.

3. Jason and Penny had caught three fish at the lake.

4. For Christmas, Kent received two shirts.

5. At the beach, she wrote her name in the sand.

6. Give this vase of flowers to your mother.

7. During the rodeo, a cowboy roped a steer.

8. A monkey grabbed the banana from his friend.

9. I answered the telephone on the first ring.

B. Directions: Cross out any prepositional phrase(s). Underline the subject once and the verb/verb phrase twice. Label any direct object(s) - D.O.

Remember: **There may be two direct objects in a sentence.**
                          D.O.   D.O.
I ate an ice cream cone and drank juice.
          This is called a compound direct object.
                          D.O.   D.O.
The mechanic fixed the tire and the fender.

1. His neighbor has made a quilt and a pillow for her grandson.

2. The lady served coffee and cake to her guests.

3. She skinned her knees and her left hand.

4. The elderly man carried an umbrella and several packages.

5. We visited a historic house and a museum in Salem.

28

Verbs

The verb of a sentence expresses an action or simply states a fact.

Examples: Jenny <u>jumped</u> onto a rubber raft.   (action)

A worker <u>dug</u> a hole for the post.   (action)

Their father <u>is</u> in the army.   (fact)

The winners <u>were</u> Cindy and Rick.   (fact)

Verbs that simply state a fact are often called **state of being verbs.**

🍓🍓🍓🍓🍓🍓🍓🍓🍓🍓🍓🍓🍓🍓🍓🍓🍓🍓🍓🍓🍓🍓🍓🍓🍓🍓🍓🍓🍓🍓🍓🍓🍓🍓

You need to memorize and learn the conjugation of *to be*:

is, am, are, was, were, be, being, been

<u>Present Tense:</u>
　　Singular*:　　is　　(A sailor <u>is</u> the winner.)
　　　　　　　　am　　(I <u>am</u> sleepy.)
　　Plural**:　　are　　(Several cows <u>are</u> near a stream.)
<u>Past Tense:</u>
　　Singular:　　was　　(A <u>sailor was</u> the winner.)
　　Plural:　　were　　(Several <u>cows were</u> near a stream.)

*Singular means one. **Plural means more than one.

29

Name_____

VERBS
Action?

Date_____

Directions: In the space provided, write <u>Yes</u> if the boldfaced verb shows action. Write
<u>No</u> if the boldfaced verb does not show action.

Example: _____No_____ He **appears** to be very happy.

1. _____ Pam **hit** the ball hard.

2. _____ A waiter **carried** a large tray on his shoulder.

3. _____ Marcy's dog **licks** my hand.

4. _____ James **is** a good athlete.

5. _____ Before breakfast, Peter **wipes** all of the counter tops.

6. _____ Mr. Potter **became** a dentist.

7. _____ Their gerbil constantly **runs** around in its cage.

8. _____ The girl **seems** sad and lonely.

9. _____ After Pioneer Days, the mayor **shaved** his beard.

10. _____ The policewoman **motioned** for us to stop.

11. _____ Her friend **was** a contestant in a beauty contest.

12. _____ A jackrabbit **jumped** beside the road.

13. _____ He **sings** in the shower.

14. _____ I **am** rather puzzled by your remark.

15. _____ I **shook** hands with Governor Jacobs.

Sometimes, it is hard to decide if a word is part of a verb (verb phrase).

     Example: Bud is glad to be an actor.

             In this sentence, is *glad* part of the verb?

If you are unsure, try placing *to* before the word: to glad. This makes it an infinitive. Then, use the word in three short sentences:

          Today, I glad.
          Yesterday, I gladded.
          Tomorrow, I shall glad.

This doesn't make sense. You can't use *glad* as a verb. Therefore, you will not underline *glad* as part of the verb.

     Example: Bud is glad (to be) an actor.

Words ending in _ly_ are usually adverbs. Occasionally, they are adjectives. Do not include a word ending in _ly_ as part of a verb.

     Example: She sleeps soundly throughout the night.

             Soundly is not part of the verb.

             She sleeps soundly ~~throughout the night~~.

Directions: Cross out any prepositional phrases.   Underline the subject once and the verb/verb phrase twice.

1. Kelly is good for her babysitter.

2. The builder talked quietly with the owner.

3. Mrs. Thomas became upset about her phone bill.

4. For a beginner, you play tennis very well.

5. During the afternoon, the children played happily in the sandbox.   31

CONTRACTIONS

"To contract" means to draw together or make smaller.   In forming contractions, we draw together two words to make a shorter word.   We insert an **apostrophe** where we have left out a letter or letters.

Suggestions:

1. Make sure that your apostrophe (**'**) is curved.   Otherwise, it may look like a chicken scratch.

2. Place an apostrophe **exactly** where the letter or letters are missing.

CONTRACTION	=	WORD	+	VERB	CONTRACTION	=	VERB	+	WORD
I'm	=	I	+	am	don't	=	do	+	not
I've	=	I	+	have	doesn't	=	does	+	not
I'd	=	I	+	would	didn't	=	did	+	not
I'll	=	I	+	shall (will)*	hasn't	=	has	+	not
you'll	=	you	+	will	hadn't	=	had	+	not
they'll	=	they	+	will	haven't	=	have	+	not
we'll	=	we	+	will	isn't	=	is	+	not
he's	=	he	+	is	aren't	=	are	+	not
he'd	=	he	+	would	wasn't	=	was	+	not
she's	=	she	+	is	weren't	=	were	+	not
that's	=	that	+	is	mustn't	=	must	+	not
they've	=	they	+	have	mightn't	=	might	+	not
it's	=	it	+	is	shouldn't	=	should	+	not
who's	=	who	+	is	couldn't	=	could	+	not
what's	=	what	+	is	wouldn't	=	would	+	not
where's	=	where	+	is	won't	=	will	+	not
here's	=	here	+	is	can't	=	can	+	not
there's	=	there	+	is					

(Can + not is written *cannot.*)

*Technically, *I shall* is correct.

Name_____

Date_____

Directions: Write the contraction in the space provided.

1. _____ Ask if **we are** allowed to water-ski with you.

2. _____ **I would** rather stay here.

3. _____ I wonder if **he is** the first contestant.

4. _____ He said, "**I am** very happy to meet you."

5. _____ **They are** headed for the Grand Canyon.

6. _____ If **she is** ready, let's go.

7. _____ **You are** standing on my foot.

8. _____ **I shall** answer his letter soon.

9. _____ Jane asked, "**What is** your new address?"

10. _____ **That is** amazing!

11. _____ **They have** no idea that he plans to visit them.

12. _____ I think that **you will** enjoy this show.

13. _____ Do you know **who is** pitching?

14. _____ **Here is** the magazine that you wanted, Melody.

15. _____ Are you aware that **it is** midnight?

Name_____   **VERBS**
                                        Contractions

Date_____

Directions: Write the contraction in the space provided.

1. _____   Lemon **had not** been added to the iced tea.

2. _____   This silverware **is not** clean.

3. _____   The porter **would not** take a tip.

4. _____   Those golfers **have not** played well lately.

5. _____   **Do not** send money in the mail.

6. _____   The minister and his wife **were not** there.

7. _____   General Grant **did not** serve at the Battle of
                               Gettysburg.

8. _____   His grandmother **will not** fly on an airplane.

9. _____   I **cannot** read that signature.

10. _____   You **are not** supposed to take your brother's
                               toys.

11. _____   The teacher **could not** tell the twins apart.

12. _____   He **has not** studied about the first permanent
                               English colony in America.

13. _____   You **must not** talk during the symphony.

14. _____   We **should not** leave before noon.

15. _____   Mark Twain **was not** the writer's real name.

You're/Your
It's/Its
They're/Their/There

A. **You're** is a contraction meaning *you are*. **Your** is a possessive pronoun; it will answer: your (what?). A quick way to check your choice is to say <u>you are</u> in the sentence.

    Examples: You're nice.
                     You are nice.   (correct)

                     Your room is messy.
                     Your what? your room
                     You are room is messy.   (Incorrect)

B. **It's** is a contraction meaning it is.   **Its** is a possessive pronoun; it will answer: your (what?).

    Examples: It's time to go.
                     It is time to go.   (correct)

                     The dog chased **its** tail.
                     Its what? its tail
                     The dog chased it is tail.   (incorrect)

C. **They're** is a contraction meaning they are.   **Their** is a possessive pronoun; it will answer their (what?).

    Examples: They're picking cherries.
                     They are picking cherries   (correct)

                     Their old car is rusty.
                     Their what? old car
                     They are old car is rusty.   (incorrect)

There is an adverb (technically telling *where*).

    Examples: I want to go there.   (Where? there)

                     There are five girls in that class.
                     There <u>are</u> five <u>girls</u> ~~in that class~~.
                     Five <u>girls</u> <u>are</u> there. (Where? there)   35

Name_____

Date_____

Directions: Circle the correct answer.

1.   (Your, You're) button is open.

2.   (They're, Their, There) uncle is a cook.

3.   (You're, Your) funny!

4.   A bird flapped (it's, its) wings and flew off.

5.   (They're, Their, There) are many trout in that stream.

6.   Do you know that (it's, its) raining?

7.   (They're, Their, There) in a hurry.

8.   (You're, Your) opinion about the crime may be correct.

9.   The club received an award for (it's, its) help in the community.

10.   The snake raised (it's, its) head and slithered away.

11.   (You're, Your) the first person to ask that question.

12.   Please ask Mrs. Dunn if she thinks (it's, its) going to rain.

13.   (They're, Their, There) ideas were not based on fact.

14.   (They're, Their, There) are many former Easterners living in Arizona.

15.   Several children threw (they're, their, there) candy wrappers on the table.

16.   The team won (it's, its) first game.

17.   If (you're, your) finished with (you're, your) chores, we can play chess.

18.   The United States is known for (it's, its) kindness toward other nations.

19.   The Johnsons want (they're, their, there) daughter to go to college.

20.   (They're, Their, There) moving to another state.

Helping (Auxiliary) Verbs:

do	has	may	can	could	is	were
does	have	might	shall	should	am	be
did	had	must	will	would	are	being
					was	been

🍓🍓🍓🍓🍓🍓🍓🍓🍓🍓🍓🍓🍓🍓🍓🍓🍓🍓🍓🍓🍓🍓🍓🍓🍓🍓🍓🍓🍓🍓🍓🍓🍓🍓

Verb Phrase:

A verb phrase is composed of one or more helping verbs plus a main verb. The main verb is the last part of a verb phrase.

Examples: I <u>must erase</u> my error.
The <u>clerk</u> <u>should have given</u> me a larger bag.

<u>verb phrase</u>	=	<u>helping verb(s)</u>	+	<u>main verb</u>
must erase	=	must	+	erase
should have given	=	should have	+	given

Name_____ **VERBS**
                                        Verb Phrases

Date_____

Remember: *Not* is an adverb. Box *not*, don't underline *not* as part of a verb phrase.

Changing an **interrogative sentence** to a declarative sentence may help you to find the subject and verb phrase.

Example: Is your friend playing soccer?

Your <u>friend is playing</u> soccer.

🍓🍓🍓🍓🍓🍓🍓🍓🍓🍓🍓🍓🍓🍓🍓🍓🍓🍓🍓🍓🍓🍓🍓🍓🍓🍓🍓🍓🍓🍓🍓🍓🍓

Directions: Cross out any prepositional phrases. Underline the subject once and the verb phrase twice. Place the helping verb(s) and the main verb on the line indicated.

Example: <u>She has visited</u> ~~for three days~~. _____has_____ _____visited_____

                                        HELPING VERB(S)   **MAIN VERB**

1. He has seen that movie twice.   _____ _____

2. You are listed in this phone book.   _____ _____

3. The train had not arrived early.   _____ _____

4. Dad must talk with the principal.   _____ _____

5. In October, we may go to the fair.   _____ _____

6. Her project was chosen by the judges. _____ _____

7. Mike's mother might shop today.   _____ _____

8. They must sell their house before June. _____ _____

9. His older brother is wearing his shirt. _____ _____

10. Can Miss Harmon play the drums?   _____ _____

38

Directions: Cross out any prepositional phrases. Underline the subject once and the verb phrase twice. Place the helping verb(s) and the main verb on the line indicated.

	HELPING VERB(S)	MAIN VERB
1. The butcher had wrapped several pork chops in white paper.	_____	_____
2. Oranges are grown in Florida.	_____	_____
3. You should have seen that parade.	_____	_____
4. May I ask you a question?	_____	_____
5. Amy will not be diving from the high diving board.	_____	_____
6. That house has been painted several times.	_____	_____
7. Would you help Kenny with his shoes?	_____	_____
8. Many trees had been planted in the forest.	_____	_____
9. Charlotte might be going to Dallas soon.	_____	_____
10. Will you hand these books to the librarian?	_____	_____

VERBS
Regular and Irregular

Verbs may be regular or irregular. This refers to how they form the past tense and past participle form.

A. Regular Verbs:

Past tense means time that has already happened. In regular verbs, ed is added to form the past tense.

The past participle is **not** a tense. It is simply a form of the verb. Place *has*, *have*, or *had* before the past participle form.

Examples:

INFINITIVE	PRESENT	PAST	PAST PARTICIPLE
to yell	yell(s)	yelled	(has, have, or had) yelled
to crawl	crawl(s)	crawled	(has, have, or had) crawled
to laugh	laugh(s)	laughed	(has, have, or had) laughed

B. Irregular Verbs:

In an irregular verb, ed is not added to the past tense or to the past participle.

Examples:

INFINITIVE	PRESENT	PAST	PAST PARTICIPLE
to sing	sings(s)	sang	(has, have, or had) sung
to ride	ride(s)	rode	(has, have, or had) ridden
to bring	bring(s)	brought	(has, have, or had) brought

40

VERBS
Regular or
Irregular?

Directions: In the space provided, write <u>RV</u> If the verb is a regular verb. Write <u>IV</u> if the
verb is an irregular verb.

1. _____   Joyce <u>sanded</u> an antique chest.

2. _____   An egg <u>broke</u> in his hand.

3. _____   The umpire <u>called</u> to the batter.

4. _____   A fish <u>swam</u> around in the pool.

5. _____   The nurse <u>helped</u> a patient out of bed.

6. _____   The accountant <u>sent</u> a bill to his client.

7. _____   The bell <u>rang</u> before school.

8. _____   Marianne <u>scooped</u> out several helpings of beans.

9. _____   The butler <u>answered</u> the door.

10. _____   Several bubbles <u>burst</u> in the air.

11. _____   We <u>climbed</u> a large oak tree.

12. _____   Someone <u>drank</u> all the milk.

13. _____   A telephone operator <u>remained</u> on the line.

14. _____   The girls <u>sneaked</u> behind their dad's chair.

15. _____   The runner <u>stole</u> second base.

16. _____   He <u>laid</u> a towel by his beach blanket.

17. _____   The museum guide <u>spoke</u> about modern art.

18. _____   They <u>swam</u> all afternoon.

19. _____   The carpenter <u>sawed</u> a piece of lumber.

20. _____   Mom <u>saw</u> Dr. Blevins at the supermarket.

IRREGULAR VERBS

Infinitive	Present	Past	Present Participle	Past Participle*
To be	is, am, are	was, were	being	been
To beat	beat(s)	beat	beating	beaten
To begin	begin(s)	began	beginning	begun
To blow	blow(s)	blew	blowing	blown
To break	break(s)	broke	breaking	broken
To bring	bring(s)	brought	bringing	brought
To burst	burst(s)	burst	bursting	burst
To buy	buy(s)	bought	buying	bought
To choose	choose(s)	chose	choosing	chosen
To come	come(s)	came	coming	come
To do	do, does	did	doing	done
To drink	drink(s)	drank	drinking	drunk
To drive	drive(s)	drove	driving	driven
To eat	eat(s)	ate	eating	eaten
To fall	fall(s)	fell	falling	fallen
To fly	fly, flies	flew	flying	flown
To freeze	freeze(s)	froze	freezing	frozen
To give	give(s)	gave	giving	given
To go	go, goes	went	going	gone
To grow	grow(s)	grew	growing	grown
To have	have, has	had	having	had
To hang	hang(s)	hanged, hung**	hanging	hanged, hung**
To know	know(s)	knew	knowing	known
To lay	lay(s)	laid	laying	laid
To leave	leave(s)	left	leaving	left

---

*Uses a helping verb such as <u>has</u>, <u>have</u>, or <u>had</u>.

**Use *hung* when referring to objects.

IRREGULAR VERBS

Infinitive	Present	Past	Present Participle	Past Participle*
To lie	lie(s)	lay	lying	lain
To ride	ride(s)	rode	riding	ridden
To ring	ring(s)	rang	ringing	rung
To rise	rises(s)	rose	rising	risen
To run	run(s)	ran	running	run
To see	see(s)	saw	seeing	seen
To set	set(s)	set	setting	set
To shake	shake(s)	shook	shaking	shaken
To sing	sing(s)	sang	singing	sung
To sink	sink(s)	sank	sinking	sunk
To sit	sit(s)	sat	sitting	sat
To speak	speak(s)	spoke	speaking	spoken
To spring	spring(s)	sprang	springing	sprung
To steal	steal(s)	stole	stealing	stolen
To swim	swim(s)	swam	swimming	swum
To swear	swear(s)	swore	swearing	sworn
To take	take(s)	took	taking	taken
To teach	teach(s)	taught	teaching	taught
To throw	throw(s)	threw	throwing	thrown
To wear	wear(s)	wore	wearing	worn
To write	write(s)	wrote	writing	written

---

*Uses a helping verb such as <u>has</u>, <u>have</u>, <u>had</u>. These may also use other helping verbs such as <u>was</u> or <u>were</u>.

Name_____

Date_____

Directions: Cross out any prepositional phrases.   Underline the subject once and the verb phrase twice.

1. Josh had (rode, ridden) his dirt bike to Corey's house.

2. I have (drunk, drank) too much water.

3. Corn is (grew, grown) in Iowa.

4. Jim had (bought, buyed) a fishing pole.

5. Jill has (went, gone) to church.

6. They had (ran, run) a mile.

7. The President of the United States was (swore, sworn) into office.

8. Those girls have (swum, swam) for an hour.

9. The pitcher had (threw, thrown) two strikes.

10. During the night, snow had (fell, fallen).

11. His pants have (shrunk, shrank) in the dryer.

12. That grass was (ate, eaten) by two goats.

13. A pirate ship had (sank, sunk) off the coast of Florida.

14. I have (saw, seen) the ship, Queen Mary.

15. Several speeches were (gave, given) before the election.

Remember: 1.   *Not* is never a verb.   Box *not.*

2.   To determine the verb phrase of a question (interrogative), change it
to a statement (declarative).   You may want to do this mentally.

ぶぶぶぶぶぶぶぶぶぶぶぶぶぶぶぶぶぶぶぶぶぶぶぶぶぶぶぶぶぶぶぶぶぶぶ

Directions: Cross out any prepositional phrases.   Underline the subject once and the
verb phrase twice.

1.   The wind had (blew, blown) throughout the night.

2.   Roses were (chose, chosen) for the bridal bouquet.

3.   You have (taught, teached) us so much.

4.   Several flags were (flown, flew) on Memorial Day.

5.   The carnival had (began, begun) at four o'clock.

6.   She has not (worn, wore) a short gown to the prom.

7.   Egg whites were beaten for the pudding.

8.   Her balloons have not (burst, busted).

9.   At Christmas, stockings are (hanged, hung) above the fireplace.

10.   The Richards family has (drove, driven) from Denver to New York City.

11.   Were ice cubes (froze, frozen) into animal shapes?

12.   At the restaurant, their cellular phone had (rung, rang).

13.   A leak has (sprang, sprung) in the pipes.

14.   Our former neighbors have (came, come) with their children.

15.   Has he (brung, brought) a sack lunch and a drink?

Name_____

Date_____

Remember: 1. *Not* is never a verb. Box *not.*

2. To determine the verb phrase of a question (interrogative), change it to a statement (declarative). You may want to do this mentally.

Directions: Cross out any prepositional phrases. Underline the subject once and the verb phrase twice.

1. The rollerbladers had (fell, fallen) three times.

2. You must have (knew, known) him for a long time.

3. A thief may have (stole, stolen) her car.

4. The choir should have (sung, sang) longer.

5. I could not have (threw, thrown) the ball again.

6. We have (hanged, hung) a picture of our great grandmother on the wall.

7. They must have (saw, seen) my sister at the mall.

8. After this piece of pie, I shall have (ate, eaten) four slices.

9. Pearl necklaces had been (gave, given) by the bride to her attendants.

10. Many pictures of that model will have been (took, taken) by the end of the session.

Date_____

☙ Part A: **Direct Objects**
Directions: Cross out any prepositional phrases. Underline the subject once and the
             verb/verb phrase twice. Label any direct object - D.O.

1. We barbecued chicken for our picnic.

2. The teenagers ate popcorn during the movie.

3. The children placed money in the offering plate.

🍓🍓🍓🍓🍓🍓🍓🍓🍓🍓🍓🍓🍓🍓🍓🍓🍓🍓🍓🍓🍓🍓🍓🍓🍓🍓🍓🍓🍓🍓🍓🍓🍓🍓

☙ Part B: *SIT/SET*
To sit means to rest.
To set means to place or put.

Infinitive	Present	Past	Present Participle	Past Participle
to sit	sit(s)	sat	sitting	(had) sat
to set	set(s)	set	setting	(had) set

To set **requires a direct object.**

Examples: I (sit, set) in the first row.
            I (<u>sit</u>, set) ~~in the first row~~. (There is no direct object. Also, I "rest" in the first row.)

            I have (sat, set) my lunch there.
                              D.O.
            <u>I</u> <u>have</u> (sat, <u>set</u>) my lunch there. (When you use *set*, you must label the direct
                                                          object. What is the object I set? Answer: lunch)

Directions: Cross out any prepositional phrases. Underline the subject once.
             Underline the verb or verb phrase twice. Label any direct object - D.O.

1. They (sat, set) with me.

2. She (sits, sets) her alarm clock at night.

3. I have (sat, set) here for a long time.

4. Dad is (sitting, setting) behind my sister.

5. The hostess has (sat, set) glasses of lemonade on the table.

6. (Sit, Set) that box under the bench.   47

Name_____

Date_____

🍓 Part A: **Direct Objects**
Directions: Cross out any prepositional phrases. Underline the subject once and the
verb/verb phrase twice. Label any direct object - <u>D.O.</u>

1. I put my cafeteria tray on the table.

2. The postman handed the package to the lady.

3. Vicki bought shoes at the department store.

🍓🍓🍓🍓🍓🍓🍓🍓🍓🍓🍓🍓🍓🍓🍓🍓🍓🍓🍓🍓🍓🍓🍓🍓🍓🍓🍓🍓🍓🍓🍓🍓🍓🍓🍓🍓🍓🍓

🍓 Part B: *RISE/RAISE*
To rise means to go up without help.
To raise means to lift or go up (with help).

Infinitive	Present	Past	Present Participle	Past Participle
to rise	rise(s)	rose	rising	(had) risen
to raise	raise(s)	raised	raising	(had) raised

To raise **requires a direct object.**

Examples: Smoke (rises, raises) in the air.
<u>Smoke</u> (<u>rises</u>, raises) ~~in the air~~. Smoke goes up on its own. Also, with *raises*,
there must be a direct object. Because <u>in the air</u>
has been crossed out, the sentence can't have a
direct object.

Mr. Clay (rose, raised) his hand.
D.O.
<u>Mr. Clay</u> (rose, <u>raised</u>) his hand. With *to raise*, a direct object is required. What
did Mr. Clay raise? Answer: hand

Directions: Cross out any prepositional phrases. Underline the subject once and the
verb or verb phrase twice. Label any direct object - <u>D.O.</u>

1. Laura (rose, raised) her glass to her lips.

2. We (rose, raised) to our feet for the prayer.

3. The sun has (risen, raised) already.
48

🍓 Part A: **Direct Objects**

Directions: Cross out any prepositional phrases. Underline the subject once and the
             verb/verb phrase twice. Label any direct object - <u>D.O.</u>

1. The dentist gave toothbrushes to her patients.

2. A mechanic lifted the hood of the car.

3. Betty's father placed the child on his shoulders.

🍓🍓🍓🍓🍓🍓🍓🍓🍓🍓🍓🍓🍓🍓🍓🍓🍓🍓🍓🍓🍓🍓🍓🍓🍓🍓🍓🍓🍓🍓🍓🍓🍓🍓🍓🍓

🍓 Part B: *LIE/LAY*

To lie means to rest.
To lay means to place.

Infinitive	Present	Past	Present Participle	Past Participle
to lay	lay(s)	laid*	laying*	(had) laid*
to lie	lie(s)	lay	lying	(had) lain

To lie means <u>to rest</u>. Try inserting "rest" when you are using *lie* in a sentence.
Lays, laid, and laying will have a direct object.

Examples:

    Ned (lies, lays) tile for a living.
                        D.O.
    <u>Ned</u> (lies, <u>lays</u>) tile ~~for a living~~.   With *lays*, you must have a direct object.

                                            What is the object Ned "places"? Answer: tile

    I had (laid, lain) on the sofa.
    <u>I had</u> (laid, <u>lain</u>) ~~on the sofa~~.   *Lain* refers to resting. I had rested on the sofa. Also,

                                            on the sofa has been crossed out. Therefore, there is
                                            no direct object. To use *laid*, there must be a direct
                                            object in the sentence.

Directions: Cross out any prepositional phrases. Underline the subject once and the
             verb or verb phrase twice. Label any direct object - <u>D.O.</u>

1. Their cat usually (lies, lays) by the front door.

2. Clark (laid, lay) his books on his bed.

3. A few cows are (lying, laying) in the field.   49

VERB TENSES:

🍓 Present Tense:
Tense means time. Present tense signifies present time. Although present can mean at this moment, it is easier to use "today" as a point of reference for present tense. Present tense never has a helping verb.

To form the present tense, remove *to* from the infinitive:

1. **If the subject is singular (one), add _s_ to the verb. (_es_ to some)**

    Examples: **to play**:   A <u>child</u> <u>plays</u> with his toys.   (one child)

    to sing: <u>She</u> <u>sings</u> constantly.   (she - one person)

2. **If the subject is <u>you</u>, <u>I</u>, or is plural (more than one), simply remove the *to* from the infinitive.**

    Examples: **to swim**:   <u>You</u> <u>swim</u> well.

    <u>I</u> <u>swim</u> daily.

    Those <u>adults</u> seldom <u>swim</u>.

🍓 Past Tense:
Past tense indicates that which has happened. Although past can mean a second ago, it is easier to use the term, "yesterday." Past tense never has a helping verb.

1. **To form the past tense of a regular verb, add <u>ed</u> to the verb.**
    to knock: knock**ed**   He <u>knock**ed**</u> on the door.
    to scrub: scrubb**ed**   We <u>scrubb**ed**</u> the floor with brushes.

2. **To form the past tense of an irregular verb, change the verb to its appropriate form.**
    to fall: **fell**   The <u>skater</u> <u>fell</u> down.
    to drive: **drove**   They <u>drove</u> a motor home.

🍓 Future Tense:
Future tense indicates time yet to happen. There are two helping verbs that indicate future tense: *shall* and *will*. Future may be any time yet to occur; however, to make it easier, we shall use "tomorrow" as a guide.

1. ***Will*** is most frequently used in forming the future tense.

2. ***Shall* is used with the pronoun, *I*.** (<u>I shall see</u> you tomorrow.)

Shall may be used with *we*.

Name_____   **VERBS**
                                          Tenses
Date_____

Directions: Read each sentence.   The verb or verb phrase has been underlined for
                    you.   Write the tense of the verb on each line.

Remember: The verb tenses are *present*, *past*, and *future*.

      Example: _____present_____   She <u>wants</u> a sled for Christmas.

1. _____   Her sister <u>pretended</u> to be angry.

2. _____   I <u>shall frost</u> this cake.

3. _____   Stephanie <u>studies</u> for tests.

4. _____   The game <u>ended</u> early.

5. _____   Large weeds <u>grow</u> in the vacant lot.

6. _____   That store <u>will open</u> at nine tomorrow.

7. _____   Micah <u>rolled</u> his sleeping bag.

8. _____   Larry often <u>makes</u> a pie for dinner.

9. _____   I <u>shall leave</u> before breakfast.

10. _____   Jenny <u>stirred</u> the pasta salad.

11. _____   Alice and I <u>love</u> board games.

12. _____   You <u>are</u> correct.

13. _____   Jason <u>hid</u> his brother's jacket.

14. _____   <u>Will</u> you please <u>help</u> me?

Name_____   **VERBS**
                                            Tenses
Date_____

Directions: Read each sentence.   The subject and verb/verb phrase have been
              underlined for you. Write the tense of the verb on each line.

Remember: The verb tenses are *present*, *past*, and *future*.

     Example: _____past_____   The <u>canoe glided</u> across the water.

1. _____   <u>Nancy attends</u> college.

2. _____   <u>Nancy will attend</u> college in the fall.

3. _____   <u>Nancy attended</u> college in Hawaii.

1. _____   Her <u>parents send</u> her brownies at Easter.

2. _____   Her <u>parents sent</u> her brownies.

3. _____   Her <u>parents will send</u> her brownies soon.

1. _____   <u>Firefighters fought</u> the blaze.

2. _____   <u>Firefighters will fight</u> the blaze.

3. _____   <u>Firefighters fight</u> blazes each summer.

1. _____   <u>I shall feed</u> the horses.

2. _____   <u>I fed</u> the horses at Uncle Ted's farm.

3. _____   <u>Uncle Ted</u> and <u>I</u> usually <u>feed</u> the horses early.

52

Directions: Cross out any prepositional phrases.   Underline the subject once and the verb/verb phrase twice. On the line provided, write the tense: *present*, *past*, or *future*.

to walk:

1. _____   He walked to the bus.

2. _____   The lady walks with her friend.

3. _____   I shall walk my dog.

to play:

1. _____   Cody and Charlene play on the swings.

2. _____   A young boy played the piano.

3. _____   The Suns will play at that arena.

to take:

1. _____   You will take a test on Thursday.

2. _____   They took their cat to the animal hospital.

3. _____   Kim takes golfing lessons.

to drink:

1. _____   I drink milk.

2. _____   A baby drank juice.

3. _____   The kitten will drink from that bowl.

53

SUBJECT VERB AGREEMENT:

The subject and verb need to agree in number in the present tense. There are several ways to do this:

A. **If the subject is singular (one), add <u>s</u> to the verb:**

> Examples: A <u>bee</u> <u>stings</u>.
>
> Her <u>friend</u> <u>leaves</u> for the Army soon.

> **Some verbs add <u>es</u>.**

> Example: The <u>juggler</u> <u>does</u> a great job.

EXCEPTIONS:

1. **Some irregular verbs completely change form for the present tense.**

> Example: A <u>nurse</u> <u>is</u> here to help.

2. **The pronoun, *I*, is singular; however, the verb does not add <u>s</u>.**

> Example: <u>I</u> <u>like</u> your new picture.

B. **If the subject is plural (more than one), do not add <u>s</u> to the verb.**

> Examples: Two <u>friends</u> <u>eat</u> lunch together.
>
> Those <u>clowns</u> <u>make</u> balloon animals.

Sometimes, the subject will be compound (two or more); do not add <u>s</u> if the subjects are joined by *and*.

> Example: His <u>grandmother</u> and <u>grandfather</u> <u>live</u> with his family.

In most irregular verbs, do not add <u>s</u> to the verb if the subject is plural.

> Example: A few <u>ladies</u> <u>hike</u> that trail often.

EXCEPTION: Some irregular verbs completely change form for the present tense.

54   Example: Those <u>cabins</u> <u>are</u> near a highway.

Directions: Read each sentence. The subject has been underlined. Circle the verb that agrees with the subject.

1. A <u>snail</u> (crawl, crawls) slowly.

2. <u>Ostriches</u> (run, runs) fast.

3. <u>Mandy</u> (has, have) a cocker spaniel puppy.

4. <u>Camels</u> (spit, spits).

5. <u>Finches</u> (make, makes) great pets.

6. <u>Each</u> of those girls (own, owns) a dog.

7. <u>Joel</u> and <u>Suzanne</u> (help, helps) at a local hospital.

8. <u>One</u> (need, needs) to listen carefully.

9. <u>Butterflies</u> (leave, leaves) a cocoon.

10. <u>We</u> (is, are) here.

11. <u>Rattlesnakes</u> (shed, sheds) their skin.

12. <u>They</u> (surf, surfs) every summer.

13. A police <u>officer</u> (watch, watches) our neighborhood carefully.

14. Date <u>palms</u> (grow, grows) in Arizona.

15. <u>Everyone</u> of the students (is, are) on the honor roll.

Name_____   **VERBS**
                                              Subject/Verb Agreement
Date_____

Directions: Read each sentence.   Underline the subject once; circle the verb that
             agrees with the subject.

Remember: You may want to cross out prepositional phrases. This helps to find the
             subject.

  1. Several mops (have, has) old handles.

  2. Those spiders (spin, spins) a large web.

  3. A yellowhammer (peck, pecks) trees.

  4. One of the boats (anchor, anchors) in Boston.

  5. His competitors (lifts, lift) heavier weights.

  6. A porbeagle (is, are) a shark with a pointed nose.

  7. The child (push, pushes) a small cart in the grocery store.

  8. Everyone of the girls (is, are) on the team.

  9. Blennies (swim, swims) in a sea.

10. Several oxen (pull, pulls) the heavy cart.

11. The tail of a racerunner (is, are) nine inches.

12. She (look, looks) through a telescope.

13. Each of the children (take, takes) a nap.

14. Maria (cook, cooks) for her entire family.

15. Many types of beans (grow, grows) in their garden.

Name_____   **Verb Review**

Date_____

A. **Contractions:**

    Directions: Write the contraction in the space provided.

1. we are - _____   6. I am -_____

2. must not - _____   7. could not - _____

3. she is - _____   8. cannot - _____

4. have not - _____   9. they have - _____

5. they are - _____   10. will not - _____

B. **Helping (Auxiliary) Verbs:**

    Directions: List the twenty-three helping verbs.

_____

_____

_____

C. **Action?:**

    Directions: Write <u>Yes</u> if the boldfaced verb shows action; write <u>No</u> if the
                  boldfaced verb does not show action.

1. _____   She **picked** flowers by the road.

2. _____   Two deer **nibble** grass in the meadow each evening.

3. _____   He **swung** the bat.

4. _____   I **need** a new toothbrush.

5. _____   She **reads** the newspaper after dinner.

6. _____   This milk **seems** sour.

D. **Regular or Irregular:**

   Directions: Write <u>RV</u> if the verb is regular. Write <u>IV</u> if the verb is irregular.

Remember: Regular verbs add <u>ed</u> to the past and past participle.

1. _____ to work   4. _____ to fly   7. _____ to write

2. _____ to land   5. _____ to help   8. _____ to be

3. _____ to slide   6. _____ to promise 9. _____ to want

E. **Subject/Verb:**

   Directions: Cross out any prepositional phrases.   Underline the subject once
                 and the verb/verb phrase twice.

   1. Tigers live in India.

   2. A trolley came toward us.

   3. We placed a saddle on the horse.

   4. That lamp shade is broken.

   5. We cleared trash along the road.

   6. Michael and Becky swim after work.

   7. The lobby of that hotel is beautiful.

   8. A large rattlesnake crawled across the desert.

   9. Many of the guests had not eaten lunch.

   10. His best outfit was ruined in the wash.

F. **Irregular Verbs:**

Directions: Circle the correct verb.

1.   A brush has (fell, fallen) behind the sink.

2.   One piece of the blueberry pie has been (ate, eaten).

3.   He has (brung, brought) a new toy.

4.   My father has (flown, flew) to Virginia.

5.   A waitress was (gave, given) a large tip.

6.   His camera has (laid, lain) on the grass all day.

7.   Have you (did, done) your errands?

8.   You must have (left, leaved) your wallet in the car.

9.   Has the runner (stole, stolen) third base?

10.   The inside of the muffin has (sunk, sank).

11.   A strong wind has (blown, blew) throughout the day.

12.   We had (saw, seen) a picture of an old castle.

13.   The gift was (boughten, bought) for ten dollars.

14.   He could have (swam, swum) two more laps.

15.   Someone had (driven, drove) over the curb.

16.   The child's condition had (began, begun) to improve.

17.   Has he (drank, drunk) his milk?

18.   He has not (rode, ridden) a jet ski.

19.   I shall have (run, ran) ten miles by Friday.

G. **Sit/Set, Rise/Raise, and Lie/Lay:**

Directions: Cross out any prepositional phrases. Underline the subject once and the verb/verb phrase twice.   Label any direct object - <u>D.O.</u>

Remember: With *to set*, *to raise*, and *to lay*, you must have a direct object. *Lays*, *laid*, and *laying* must have a direct object.

1. I (raised, rose) my hand.

2. The cord is (lying, laying) on the floor.

3. The bread has (raised, risen) in a warm spot.

4. Mom had (laid, lain) the photographs on the desk.

5. The house (sits, sets) on a cliff.

6. Her secretary (lies, lays) the office mail on a file cabinet.

7. Grandpa always (sits, sets) firewood by the fireplace.

H. **Tenses:**

Directions: Cross out any prepositional phrases. Underline the subject once and the verb/verb phrase twice. Write the tense on the line.

Remember: The tenses that we have learned are **present**, **past**, and **future**.

1. _____   A jackrabbit hopped in the road.

2. _____   Our nation's capital is Washington, D.C.

3. _____   My cousin will cook hot dogs for us.

4. _____   Our dog lies on her stomach.

5. _____   Kent watched the parade.

6. _____   The potter will use his wheel.

7. _____   Jacob came for a visit.

8. _____   I shall read to you.

I. **Helping Verb(s) + Main Verb:**
   Directions: Cross out any prepositional phrases. Underline the subject once and the verb/verb phrase twice.   Write the helping verb(s) and the main verb on the lines.

	Helping Verb(s)	**Main Verb**

1.   We must leave soon.   _____ _____

2.   A coyote has run across the road.   _____ _____

3.   A window washer was finished.   _____ _____

4.   I should have gone with you.   _____ _____

5.   Did you receive a trophy?   _____ _____

J. **You're/Your, It's/Its, and They're/Their/There:**
   Directions: Circle the correct word.

1.   Does (you're, your) bird have water?
2.   If (you're, your) going, please hurry.
3.   A cow lifted (it's, its) head and mooed.
4.   Janice said that (it's, its) difficult to use the balance beam.
5.   (They're, Their, There) brother lives in Idaho.
6.   (They're, Their, There) are several dirty dishes in the sink.
7.   Let's ask when (they're, their, there) boarding the airplane.

K. **Subject/Verb Agreement:**
   Directions: Select the correct verb.

1.   A penguin (waddle, waddles) over the snow.
2.   They (pick, picks) peaches at an orchard.
3.   Fresh marshmallows (is, are) in the cupboard.
4.   One of the boys (need, needs) a hair cut.
5.   Geysers (spurts, spurt) water at that national park.
6.   My friend (go, goes) to the Ozark Mountains each summer.

Name_____

Date_____

A. **Preposition List:**

   Directions: List the forty prepositions that you have learned.

1. _____   16. _____   31. _____

2. _____   17. _____   32. _____

3. _____   18. _____   33. _____

4. _____   19. _____   34. _____

5. _____   20. _____   35. _____

6. _____   21. _____   36. _____

7. _____   22. _____   37. _____

8. _____   23. _____   38. _____

9. _____   24. _____   39. _____

10. _____   25. _____   40. _____

11. _____   26. _____

12. _____   27. _____

13. _____   28. _____

14. _____   29. _____

15. _____   30. _____

B. **Object of the Preposition:**

   Directions: Cross out any prepositional phrases. Label the object of the
                 preposition - O.P.

1.   The tree trimmer climbed on a ladder.

2.   His house is near a creek.

3.   A bee buzzed around my head.

C. **Compound Subjects:**

> Directions: Cross out any prepositional phrases. Underline the subject once and the verb/verb phrase twice.

Remember: Compound means more than one.

1. Miss Putnam or Mrs. Poe lives in Rhode Island.

2. Opossums and monkeys hang by their tails.

3. His socks, jersey, and shorts are in the washing machine.

D. **Imperative Sentences:**

> Directions: Cross out any prepositional phrases. Underline the subject once and the verb/verb phrase twice.

Remember: An imperative sentence gives a command.

1. Stay with me.

2. Pass the bread, please.

3. Write in black ink.

E. **Compound Objects of the Preposition:**

> Directions: Cross out any prepositional phrases. Underline the subject once and the verb/verb phrase twice.

Remember: Compound means more than one.

1. We drew pictures with crayons and colored pencils.

2. That package is for Jim and Jan.

3. A volunteer handed booklets to Dawn and me.

F. **Compound Verbs:**

    Directions: Cross out any prepositional phrases. Underline the subject once
                  and the verb/verb phrase twice.

Remember: Compound means more than one.

1.   A seal yelps and claps.

2.   A spectator waved her hands and cheered.

3.   A teenager stomped his foot and muttered.

G.   **Infinitives:**

    Directions: Cross out any prepositional phrases. Underline the subject once
                  and the verb twice. Place an infinitive in parenthesis ( ).

Remember: To + a verb = infinitive.   Do not cross out any infinitives.

    Examples: to run
                to taste

1.   You seem to be angry.

2.   We like to feed ducks at the park.

3.   Their sister started to drive.

H.   **Prepositions:**

    Directions: Cross out any prepositional phrases. Underline the subject once
                  and the verb/verb phrase twice. Label any direct object - <u>D.O.</u>

1.   Allen writes letters to his friends.

2.   I set the broom beside the back door.

3.   Mr. Scott took a trip with a friend.

NOUNS

A. **Definition:** **A noun names a person, place, thing, or idea.**

    Examples:

        person: Judy, aunt, teacher, dentist, George Washington

        place: park, beach, zoo, Washington, D.C.

        thing: knife, rose, mustard

        idea: happiness, love, knowledge

B. **Concrete and Abstract Nouns:**

1. **Concrete nouns can be seen:**   **book, camera, tree.**

   Some concrete nouns cannot "technically" be seen unless they are examined in very small parts called atoms. Examples of this are *air* and *wind.*

2. **Abstract nouns are those that cannot be seen.** They usually represent an idea. Examples of abstract nouns are ***love*** and ***kindness***.

Name_____

Date_____

Directions: Each set contains a concrete noun and an abstract noun. In the space provided, write C if the noun is concrete and A if the noun is abstract.

A.
1. _____   drum

2. _____   love

B.
1. _____   happiness

2. _____   plant

C.
1. _____   fun

2. _____   bread

D.
1. _____   time

2. _____   basket

E.
1. _____   sand

2. _____   joy

F.
1. _____   tongue

2. _____   freedom

G.
1. _____   hope

2. _____   fan

H.
1. _____   bear

2. _____   fear

I.
1. _____   courage

2. _____   cream

J.
1. _____   applesauce

2. _____   kindness

K.
1. _____   air

2. _____   faith

L.
1. _____   friendship

2. _____   raft

COMMON AND PROPER NOUNS

A common noun does not name a specific person, place, or thing. Most nouns are common. Do not capitalize common nouns.

Examples: person: boy, girl, cousin, nurse, mayor

place: park, zoo, ceiling

thing: egg, rope, train

Types of common nouns are still common and are not capitalized.

Examples:

common noun	type (common noun)
flower	daisy
dog	terrier
horse	palomino
building	tower

A proper noun names a specific person, place, or thing. Capitalize a proper noun.

common noun	proper noun
boy	Gary
girl	Sarah
cat	Whiskers
doctor	Dr. Jones
park	Green Park
zoo	San Diego Zoo
train	Oriental Express

Name_____

Date_____

Directions: Write a proper noun for each common noun.

A.
1. common noun: state

2. proper noun: _____

B.
1. common noun: country

2. proper noun: _____

C.
1. common noun: lake

2. proper noun: _____

D.
1. common noun: mountain

2. proper noun: _____

E.
1. common noun: day

2. proper noun: _____

F.
1. common noun: month

2. proper noun: _____

G.
1. common noun: town

2. proper noun: _____

H.
1. common noun: street

2. proper noun: _____

I.
1. common noun: holiday

2. proper noun: _____

J.
1. common noun: river

2. proper noun: _____

K.
1. common noun: school

2. proper noun: _____

L.
1. common noun: hospital

2. proper noun: _____

M.
1. common noun: store

2. proper noun: _____

N.
1. common noun: church

2. proper noun: _____

NOUN DETERMINERS

Determiners are words that signal that a noun may follow. They simply help you to identify nouns in a sentence. Determiners are stop signs. When you see a determiner, stop and check if a noun follows it.

Classification of Determiners:

1. **Articles: a, an, the**

   Example: **The** <u>tire</u> is flat.

2. **Demonstratives: this, that, those, these**

   Example: Do you like **this** <u>gum</u>?

3. **Numbers**

   Example: **Two** <u>boys</u> laughed and cheered.

4. **Possessive pronouns: my, his, her, your, its, our, their, whose**

   Example: **My** <u>cousin</u> is **your** <u>neighbor</u>.

5. **Possessive nouns:**

   Example: Has the **<u>dog's</u>** <u>leash</u> been found?

   Note: Both the word that owns (*dog's*) and the noun that it owns (*leash*) are considered nouns. Underline both as nouns.

6. **Indefinites: some, few, many, several, no, any**

   Example: **Several** <u>guests</u> arrived.

IMPORTANT: There may be two determiners before a noun.

Her first <u>tooth</u> came in.

IMPORTANT: There may be determiner + descriptive word or words before the noun.

A *large white* <u>cake</u> had been made.

IMPORTANT: There may be nouns without determiners in a sentence. Always look for any word that states a person, place, thing, or idea.

<u>Dad</u> and **his** <u>friend</u> went to <u>Seattle.</u>

69

Name_____   **NOUNS**
                                        Determiners
Date_____

Classification of Determiners:
1.   Articles: **a, an, the**
2.   Demonstratives: **this, that, those, these**
3.   Numbers: Example: **fifty** people
4.   Possessive pronouns: **my, his, her, your, its, our, their, whose**
5.   Possessive nouns: Example: **Joyce's** car
6.   Indefinites: **some, few, many, several, no, any**

Directions: A determiner appears in boldfaced print. Find the noun that it determines.
              Write both the determiner and the noun on the line.

          Example: Is **your** toe broken? ____your toe____

1.   **Kim's** tricycle is red.   _____

2.   **Her** aunt arrived today.   _____

3.   Where is **the** fan?   _____

4.   **Five** puppies were born.   _____

5.   **Many** tourists come here.   _____

6.   He bought **an** umbrella.   _____

7.   Please hand me **that** knife.   _____

8.   **This** day has been fun.   _____

9.   **Grandpa's** back hurts.   _____

10. I took **my** temperature.   _____

11. **Several** hikers rested.   _____

12. We ate **three** pies.   _____

13. Is **your** watch new?   _____

14. **These** stones are smooth.   _____

70

Classification of Determiners:
1. Articles: **a, an, the**
2. Demonstratives: **this, that, those, these**
3. Numbers: Example: **fifty** people
4. Possessive pronouns: **my, his, her, your, its, our, their, whose**
5. Possessive nouns: Example: **Joyce's** car
6. Indefinites: **some, few, many, several, no, any**

Directions: Circle each determiner. Underline the noun that follows each determiner.

Example: (The) cat licked (its) paw.

1. The tree is beside a stream.

2. This machine gives no change.

3. Does your grandmother live on an island?

4. Some people hunt in those woods.

5. Their friend lives five houses away.

6. Several ducklings waddled after their mother.

7. Susan's hair is below her waist.

8. Whose cap was left on the porch?

9. Marilyn's son washes his car in an hour.

10. Few cheerleaders stayed for a meeting.

11. Place these bananas in Ted's sack.

12. That baby has her first tooth.

13. Many campers prefer a shady spot.

14. Is Laura's gerbil in its cage?

15. A cobbler repaired four shoes.

SINGULAR AND PLURAL NOUNS

Singular means one.

Plural means more than one.

Rule 1: The **plural of most nouns** is made by adding **s** to the singular form.

    comb   kite
    combs   kites

Rule 2: When a singular noun ends in **s**, **sh**, **ch**, **x**, or **z**, add **es** to form the plural.

bus	flash	patch	six	fuzz
buses	flashes	patches	sixes	fuzzes

Rule 3: When a singular noun ends in a **vowel + y** (**ay**, **ey**, **iy**, **oy**, or **uy**), add **s** to form the plural.

day	donkey	toy	guy
days	donkeys	toys	guys

Rule 4: When a singular noun ends in a **consonant + y**, change the **y to i** and add **es**.

lady	berry	baby
ladies	berries	babies

Rule 5: Some nouns totally change in the plural form.

man	child	goose
men	children	geese

🍓🍓 **Use a dictionary to determine the plural form of nouns.**

In a dictionary, *pl* or *pl.* = plural

72

If the word changes to form the plural, the dictionary will spell out the plural.

Example: child (chīld) n., *pl.* **children**   1. baby or infant

If two spellings are given, the first is preferred.

Example: cac tus (kak´tus) n., *pl.* **cacti, cactuses**
The dictionary may also give the endings as: *pl.* **ti** or **tuses**.

Rule 6: Some nouns are the same in singular and plural forms.

deer	moose
deer	moose

🍓🍓 <u>**Use a dictionary to determine the plural form of nouns.**</u>

In a dictionary, *pl* or *pl.* = plural

If two spellings are given, the first is preferred.

Example: doe (dō) n., *pl.* **doe or does**

Rule 7: Some nouns ending in <u>**f**</u>, change the <u>**f**</u> to <u>**v**</u> and add <u>**es**</u> to form the plural.

loa**f**	cal**f**
loaves	calves

🍓🍓 <u>**Use a dictionary to determine the plural form.**</u>

If a noun changes from <u>**f**</u> to <u>**v**</u> in the plural, the dictionary will show it.

Example: loaf (lōf) n., *pl.* loaves   1. a shaped mass of bread

When two spellings are given for the plural, the first is preferred.

Example: hoof (hōof) n., *pl.* **hoofs** or **hooves**

Rule 8: Some nouns ending in **f** do not change. They simply add **s**.

roof	proof
roofs	proofs

🍓🍓 <u>**Use a dictionary to determine the plural form of nouns.**</u>

Rule 9: Some nouns ending in **o**, add **s** to form the plural.

yo-yo	piano
yo-yos	pianos

Some nouns ending in **o** add **es** to form the plural.

tomato	potato
tomatoes	potatoes

Some nouns ending in **o** add **s** or **es** to form the plural.

hobo	zero
hoboes or hobos	zeros or zeroes

When two spellings are provided, the first is preferred.

> **Note:** Notice that the preferred spelling for hobo adds **es** where the preferred spelling of the plural form of zero simply adds **s**. **Always use a dictionary.**

Rule 10: Some hyphenated nouns add **s** to the first part when forming the plural.

father-in-law
fathers-in-law

Some non-hyphenated words that serve as a singular noun add **s** to the first part when forming the plural.

editor in chief
editors in chief

74   🍓🍓<u>**Use a dictionary to determine the plural form of nouns.**</u>

Name_____

Date_____

Directions: Write the plural form in the space provided.

Remember: A.   You may use the rules found on pages 169-171.

B.   You may use a dictionary.

1. bill - _____

2. yo-yo - _____

3. mouse - _____

4. horse - _____

5. key - _____

6. ruby - _____

7. paw - _____

8. tooth - _____

9. wife - _____

10. child - _____

11. blueberry - _____

12. wish - _____

13. man - _____

14. pinch - _____

15. class - _____

Name_____   **NOUNS**
                                          Plurals

Date_____

Directions: Write the plural form in the space provided.

Remember: A.   You may use the rules found on pages 169-171.

B.   You may use a dictionary.

1. day - _____

2. fly - _____

3. reef - _____

4. fez - _____

5. foot - _____

6. monkey - _____

7. sheep - _____

8. dish - _____

9. sister-in law - _____

10. scratch - _____

11. tree - _____

12. half - _____

13. mix - _____

14. cartoon - _____

15. tomato - _____
76

POSSESSIVE NOUNS

To possess means to own.
> Example: Tansy's house

Possessive nouns can show that something belongs to an item.
> Example: the chair's back

Possessive nouns can show that something is shared.
> Example: the joggers' path

Possessive nouns can show that an item contains something.
> Example: the well's water

Possessive nouns can show that someone is using something.
> Example: an artist's canvas

❦❦❦❦❦❦❦❦❦❦❦❦❦❦❦❦❦❦❦❦❦❦❦❦❦❦❦❦❦❦❦❦❦❦❦❦❦❦

There are three simple rules for forming the possessive:

Rule 1: To form the possessive of a **singular** noun, **add 's**.

> Examples: a truck belonging to Rana: Rana**'s** truck
>
> lid on a jar: a jar**'s** lid
>
> shoes belonging to Elias: Elias**'s** shoes

Important: It does not matter with what letter the word ends. A singular noun adds **'s** to form the possessive.

Rule 2: To form the possessive of a **plural** noun **ending in s**, add **'** after the **s**.

> Examples: a barn belonging to several horses: horse**s'** barn
>
> dishes shared by two cats: cat**s'** dishes

Rule 3: To form the possessive of a **plural** noun **not ending in s**, add **'s**.

> Examples: a dessert shared by two children: children's dessert
>
> a bathroom used by many women: women's bathroom

Name_____

Date_____

Directions: Write the possessive noun and the item in the space provided.

Example: a baton belonging to a twirler: _____ twirler's baton _____

Remember:
1. If a noun is singular (one), add **'s**.

2. If a noun is plural (more than one) and ends in **s**, add **'**.

3. If a noun is plural and does **not** end in **s**, add **'s**.

1. a robe than belongs to a man

_____

2. a sweater belonging to her sister

_____

3. shoes that belong to Philip

_____

4. a book that is shared by several teachers

_____

5. diamonds that are in a ring

_____

6. a bicycle belonging to James

_____

7. a sailboat belonging to more than one woman

78 _____

Name_____

Date_____

Directions: Write the possessive noun and the item in the space provided.

Example: a baton belonging to a twirler: _____twirler's baton_____

Remember:
1. If a noun is singular (one), add **'s**.

2. If a noun is plural (more than one) and ends in **s**, add **'**.

3. If a noun is plural and does **not** end in **s**, add **'s**.

🍓🍓🍓🍓🍓🍓🍓🍓🍓🍓🍓🍓🍓🍓🍓🍓🍓🍓🍓🍓🍓🍓🍓🍓🍓🍓🍓🍓🍓🍓🍓🍓🍓🍓

1.   a conference attended by attorneys

_____

2.   a cast belonging to Peter

_____

3.   a path shared by runners

_____

4.   hamsters belonging to Frances

_____

5.   a lunch shared by two boys

_____

6.   a play for children

_____

7.   holes in a shirt

_____

A. **Definition:**

Directions: Fill in the blanks.

A noun names a _____, _____, _____, or

_____.

B. **Concrete and Abstract Nouns:**

Directions: Write <u>C</u> if the noun is concrete; write <u>A</u> if the noun is abstract.

1. _____ parrot	5. _____ gravy	9. _____ air
2. _____ honesty	6. _____ salt	10. _____ tile
3. _____ truth	7. _____ love	11. _____ joy
4. _____ tar	8. _____ happiness	12. _____ log

C. **Common and Proper Nouns:**

Directions: Write <u>C</u> if the noun is common; write <u>P</u> is the noun is proper.

1. _____ BRIAN	5. _____ OCEAN	9. _____ SOAP
2. _____ COMPUTER	6. _____ MOTEL	10. _____ UTAH
3. _____ ATLANTA	7. _____ MEXICO	11. _____ COW
4. _____ SKUNK CREEK	8. _____ BARTLETT LAKE	12. _____ BIRD

Date_____

A.   **Noun Determiners:**

       Directions: Fill in the blank.

1.   The three articles that are noun determiners are_____,_____, and_____.

2.   The four demonstrative determiners are_____,_____,
      _____, and_____.

3.   Write an example of a number used as a determiner.
      _____

4.   The possessive pronouns that can serve as determiners are_____,_____,
      _____,_____,_____,_____,_____, and_____.

5.   Write an example of a possessive noun used as a determiner.

      _____

6.   Write three examples of indefinites that can serve as determiners:_____,
      _____, and_____.

B.   **Noun Identification:**

       Directions: Underline any nouns in each sentence.

Remember: You may wish to circle determiners to help you find most nouns.

1.   His company is in an airpark.

2.   Gary's sister has two puppies.

3.   Several trees line that street.

4.   Does their niece go to a university?

5.   Your hot dog is burned in the middle.

6.   These pants were three dollars at a yard sale.

7.   Many fashions were shown during the show in Dallas.

Name_____   **Noun Review**

Date_____

F. **Singular and Plural Nouns:**
   Directions: Write the plural.

1. pony - _____

2. roll - _____

3. watch - _____

4. leaf - _____

5. potato - _____

6. cactus - _____

7. blade - _____

8. die - _____

9. country - _____

10. puff - _____

11. man - _____

12. piano - _____

G. **Possessive Nouns**
   Directions: Write the possessive form.

1. slippers that belong to their mother

_____

2. house that belongs to Harvey

_____

3. vacation taken by three girls

_____

4. a party given by more than one lady

_____

5. a notebook belonging to Chris

_____

6. organization belonging to more than one man

_____

Name_____

Date_____

A. **Preposition List:**

Directions: List forty prepositions.

1. _____	16. _____	31. _____
2. _____	17. _____	32. _____
3. _____	18. _____	33. _____
4. _____	19. _____	34. _____
5. _____	20. _____	35. _____
6. _____	21. _____	36. _____
7. _____	22. _____	37. _____
8. _____	23. _____	38. _____
9. _____	24. _____	39. _____
10. _____	25. _____	40. _____
11. _____	26. _____	
12. _____	27. _____	
13. _____	28. _____	
14. _____	29. _____	
15. _____	30. _____	

B. **Object of the Preposition:**
Directions: Cross out any prepositional phrases. Label the object of the preposition - O.P.

1. A ground hog emerged from his hole.

2. My tether ball is tied with a rope.

C. **Compound Subject:**

>   Directions: Cross out any prepositional phrases. Underline the subject once
>   and the verb/verb phrase twice.

Remember: Compound means more than one.

1. Martha and her mother shop at a nearby supermarket.

2. During the spring, tulips and irises bloom in their garden.

3. A mare and her colt stood quietly beside a rippling stream.

🍓🍓🍓🍓🍓🍓🍓🍓🍓🍓🍓🍓🍓🍓🍓🍓🍓🍓🍓🍓🍓🍓🍓🍓🍓🍓🍓🍓🍓🍓🍓🍓🍓🍓

D. **Imperative Sentences:**

>   Directions: Cross out any prepositional phrases. Underline the subject once
>   and the verb/verb phrase twice.

Remember: An imperative sentence gives a command.

1. Smile.

2. Mail our letters at the post office, please.

🍓🍓🍓🍓🍓🍓🍓🍓🍓🍓🍓🍓🍓🍓🍓🍓🍓🍓🍓🍓🍓🍓🍓🍓🍓🍓🍓🍓🍓🍓🍓🍓🍓🍓

E. **Compound Objects of the Preposition:**

>   Directions: Cross out any prepositional phrases. Underline the subject once
>   and the verb/verb phrase twice.

Remember: Compound means more than one.

1. Place the boxes against that wall and this door.

2. A package arrived from Don and Joy.

3. Flies swarmed around Brian, Terry, and me.

84

F. **Compound Verbs:**

Directions: Cross out any prepositional phrases. Underline the subject once
and the verb/verb phrase twice.

Remember: Compound means more than one.

1.   Before a meal, we wash our hands and dry them.

2.   The doctor looked at the chart and smiled at his patient.

G.   **Infinitives:**

Directions: Cross out any prepositional phrases. Underline the subject once
and the verb twice. Place an infinitive in parenthesis (   ).

Remember: To + a verb = infinitive.   Do not cross out any infinitives.

1.   His sister wants to be an actress.

2.   Jenny forgot to go to the dentist.

H.   **Prepositions:**

Directions: Cross out any prepositional phrases. Underline the subject once
and the verb/verb phrase twice. Label any direct object - D.O.

1.   After the birthday party, Mother washed the table.

2.   The orthodontist put braces on Jill's teeth.

3.   A detective searched the office for clues about the recent theft.

4.   Many of the players tossed footballs before the game.

5.   Her guest brought her candy and flowers.

I. Contractions:

Directions: Write the contraction in the space provided.

1. should not - _____   6. you are - _____

2. I shall - _____   7. who is - _____

3. is not - _____   8. will not - _____

4. we are - _____   9. they have - _____

5. they will - _____   10. it is - _____

🍓🍓🍓🍓🍓🍓🍓🍓🍓🍓🍓🍓🍓🍓🍓🍓🍓🍓🍓🍓🍓🍓🍓🍓🍓🍓🍓🍓🍓🍓🍓🍓

J. Helping (Auxiliary) Verbs:

Directions: List the twenty-three helping verbs.

_____

_____

_____

🍓🍓🍓🍓🍓🍓🍓🍓🍓🍓🍓🍓🍓🍓🍓🍓🍓🍓🍓🍓🍓🍓🍓🍓🍓🍓🍓🍓🍓🍓🍓🍓

K. Action?:

Directions: Write Yes if the boldfaced verb shows action; write No if the
            boldfaced verb does not show action.

1. _____   The comic **laughed** at his own jokes.

2. _____   That clerk **appears** to be confused.

3. _____   A customer **tasted** several types of cheese.

4. _____   Those fishing nets **have** too many rips.

86

L. **Regular or Irregular:**

Directions: Write <u>RV</u> if the verb is regular.   Write <u>IV</u> if the verb is irregular.

Remember: Regular verbs add <u>ed</u> to the past and past participle.

1. _____ to drive   3. _____ to say   5. _____ to stir

2. _____ to paste   4. _____ to float   6. _____ to freeze

M. **Subject/Verb:**

Directions: Cross out any prepositional phrases.   Underline the subject once and the verb/verb phrase twice.

1. Her speech is about the dangers of smoking.

2. A cordless telephone is under the bed.

3. The temperature has fallen below zero.

N. **Tenses:**

Directions: Cross out any prepositional phrases. Underline the subject once and the verb/verb phrase twice. Write the tense on the line.

Remember: The tenses that we have learned are *present*, *past*, and *future*.

1. _____   Cadets march in several parades each year.

2. _____   We mopped the floor with several old cloths.

3. _____   Mt. Fuji is in Japan.

4. _____   Jamie will go to Montana tomorrow.

O. **Irregular Verbs:**

Directions: Select the correct verb.

1. The dog had (shook, shaken) itself.

2. Our bus has (came, come) early.

3. We were (gave, given) another chance.

4. He had already (did, done) his assignment.

5. A car had been (stolen, stole) during the night.

6. They were (chose, chosen) to be leaders.

P. **Sit/Set, Rise/Raise, and Lie/Lay:**

Directions: Cross out any prepositional phrases. Underline the subject once
and the verb/verb phrase twice.   Label any direct object - <u>D.O.</u>

Remember: With *to set*, *to raise*, and *to lay*, you must have a direct object.
Lays, *laid*, and *laying* must have a direct object.

1. The principal (sits, sets) on stage during graduation ceremonies.

2. She (rises, raises) early in the morning.

3. The florist (lay, laid) several roses on the counter.

Q. **Subject-Verb Agreement:**

Directions: Circle the verb that agrees with the subject.

1. Zek (like, likes) to blow bubbles.

2. Mr. Hobbs and his wife (play, plays) tennis daily.

3. Peaches (grow, grows) in that area of Pennsylvania.

4. One of the boys (swim, swims) on a team.

SENTENCE TYPES

There are four types of sentences.

1. A **declarative** sentence makes a statement. A declarative sentence ends with a period.

    Examples: John Glenn was one of our first astronauts.

    This caramel apple tastes good.

    Paseo Verde Elementary School is new.

2. An **interrogative** sentence asks a question. An interrogative sentence ends with a question mark.

    Examples: Have you ever been to a fair?

    What's your name?

    Did your friend move to Iowa?

3. An **imperative** sentence gives a command. An imperative sentence ends with a period.

    Examples: Put this in the kitchen, please.

    Write your name on the paper.

    Eat before you leave.

4. An **exclamatory sentence** shows emotion. An exclamatory sentence ends with an exclamation point (mark).

    Examples: The ice cream man is here!

    Stop!

    Slow Down! You're driving too fast!

89

Name_____   **SENTENCE   TYPES**

Date_____

Directions: Write the sentence type.

Example: ____declarative_____   His neighbor is an engineer.

1. _____   Is Dover in Delaware?

2. _____   That table has been sanded well.

3. _____   We did it!

4. _____   Wait for me, please.

5. _____   Must I come along?

6. _____   Pilgrims arrived on the ship, Mayflower.

7. _____   Place the chicken on the grill.

8. _____   Will the doctor see us today?

9. _____   I am so surprised!

10. _____   No! We lost again!

11. _____   A torn kite lay by the side of the road.

12. _____   Todd asked if we could go with him.

13. _____   Don't touch that.

14. _____   Can you snorkel?

15. _____   Niagara Falls is on the Canadian border.

Conjunctions are joining words.

The three coordinating conjunctions are *and*, *but*, and *or*.

Examples: Bob **and** Gerald are friends.

You may have ice cream **or** sherbet.

Julie likes Phoenix, **but** it's hot there in the summer.

Directions: Circle any conjunctions.

1.   Strawberries and ice cream were served.

2.   Molly or Misty will come with us.

3.   They like to sail, but they get seasick.

4.   The sergeant stopped and saluted.

5.   Michael likes to read mysteries or science fiction.

6.   Marsha and her brother seldom visit their grandparents or cousins.

7.   The restaurant takes cash or credit cards but no checks.

8.   Penny and her mother laughed but looked upset.

9.   Have Tom and Cindy decided to marry in December.

10. You may choose to dust or to vacuum, but you must do one.

Name_____

Date_____

An interjection is a word or phrase (more than one word) that shows strong emotion. An interjection ends with an exclamation point (mark).

Examples: Yeah!

Oh rats!

If an expression has both a subject and a verb, it is an **exclamatory sentence**, not an interjection.

Example: Stop!

(You) Stop!

Directions: Circle any interjections.

1. Hurrah! Our team is winning!

2. Wow! That car is really neat!

3. Oh! The gas tank is nearly empty!

4. We won! Yippee!

5. No! I don't believe it!

6. This milk is sour! Yuck!

7. Yeah! The flight is arriving!

8. Ouch! I've burned my finger!

9. Yikes! You scared me!

10. I'd love to go! Thanks!

ADJECTIVES

There are two major types of adjectives: limiting and descriptive.
You have used limiting adjectives when studying nouns. They were called determiners or determining adjectives.

Limiting Adjectives = Determiners = Determining Adjectives

Limiting (Determining) Adjectives:

1. **Articles: a, an, the**

    Example: **The** bank has closed.

2. **Demonstratives: this, that, those, these**

    Example: Are **those** hangers plastic?

3. **Numbers**

    Example: **Thirteen** students were in the play.

4. **Possessive pronouns: my, his, her, your, its, our, their, whose**

    Example: **Whose** umbrella is missing?

5. **Possessive nouns:**

    Example: **Dan's** friend is a stewardess.

6. **Indefinites: some, few, many, several, no, any**

    Example: I'd like a **few** peanuts, please.

An adjective modifies another word. *Modifies* means *to go over to*. In very simple terms, an adjective answers *what*.

    Example: That hat is dirty.

    That is an adjective. *That what? That hat.* *That* is an adjective modifying *hat*.

Sometimes, a word that can be an adjective will appear alone in a sentence. When this happens, the word will not serve as an adjective.

    Example: That is unusual.

    That what? We don't know. In this sentence, *that* is not an adjective.

93

Limiting (Determining) Adjectives:

1. **Articles: a, an, the**
2. **Demonstratives: this, that, those, these**
3. **Numbers**
4. **Possessive pronouns: my, his, her, your, its, our, their, whose**
5. **Possessive nouns**
6. **Indefinites: some, few, many, several, no, any**

🍓🍓🍓🍓🍓🍓🍓🍓🍓🍓🍓🍓🍓🍓🍓🍓🍓🍓🍓🍓🍓🍓🍓🍓🍓🍓🍓🍓🍓🍓🍓

Directions: Circle any limiting adjective. Draw an arrow from the adjective to the word
it modifies (goes over to).

Example: (My) uncle fishes for bass.

1.   That person is nice.

2.   He spent three dollars.

3.   No rain fell.

4.   Who ate our brownies?

5.   Jim's brother works with him.

6.   Do you want these magazines?

7.   The first batter was Stacy.

8.   His aunt writes children's stories.

9.   Several pencils are on the table.

10.   A trophy was given to their father.

Name_____

ADJECTIVES
Limiting Adjectives

Date_____

Directions: Write <u>Yes</u> if the boldfaced word serves as a limiting adjective; write
<u>No</u> if the boldfaced word does not serve as a limiting adjective.

Remember: If a word serves as a limiting adjective, it will modify (go over to)
another word (noun).

Example: <u>Yes</u> **This** shoe is made of leather. *This what? This shoe!*

1. _____ **Many** students are learning Spanish.

2. _____ **Many** will attend next week's meeting.

3. _____ Do you want **these** straws?

4. _____ **These** belong to you.

5. _____ There are **few** lights in the new park.

6. _____ **Few** decided to stay.

7. _____ They own **two** cars.

8. _____ Only **two** raised their hands.

9. _____ **This** isn't working.

10. _____ Will you work on **this** project with me?

11. _____ **Whose** is this?

12. _____ **Whose** truck is parked in the driveway?

13. _____ I don't have time for **that**.

14. _____ **That** mountain is very rugged.

DESCRIPTIVE ADJECTIVES

Most adjectives describe.

Adjectives modify (go over to) nouns or pronouns.

Most adjectives describe nouns.

Generally, we may say that descriptive adjectives tell **what kind**.

Specifically, they may tell color, type, condition, size, etc.

You know how to identify a noun. Look for any word or words that describe that noun.

Examples: **new** car

New tells *what kind* of car. *New* specifically tells the <u>condition</u> of the car.

yellow car

Yellow tells *what kind* of car. *Yellow* specifically tells the <u>color</u> of the car.

antique car

Antique tells *what kind* of car. *Antique* specifically tells the <u>type</u> of car.

compact car

Compact tells what kind of car. *Compact* specifically tells the <u>size</u> of the car.

🍓Often, more than one adjective will precede a noun (or pronoun).

An **enormous yellow** <u>balloon</u> was hanging from a **tall, steel** <u>post</u>.

(Notice that you do not need a comma between the two descriptive adjectives if one adjective is a color.)

🍓An adjective may occur after the verb and go back to describe the subject.

That <u>baby is</u> **cute**.   *cute* baby

🍓Adjectives may occur after a noun (or pronoun).

96   Her bathing suit, **sandy** and **wet**, lay on the floor.

Name_____

Date_____

1. Colors describe.

Directions: Write a color before each item.   Use a color once.

Example: _____purple_____ crayon

a. _____ cat   c. _____ car

b. _____ sky   d. _____ house

2. Words that show size describe.

Directions: Write a word that shows size before each item.   Use a word once.

Example: _____tiny_____ flower

a. _____ bee   c. _____ tree

b. _____ store   d. _____ dog

3. Words that show condition describe.

Directions: Write a word that shows condition before each item. Use a word once.

Example: _____holey_____ shirt

a. _____ shoes   c. _____ truck

b. _____ play   d. _____ candy

3. Words that show "type of" describe.

Directions: Write a word that shows a "type of" before each item.

Example: _____credit_____ card

a. _____ school   c. _____ band

b. _____ beans   d. _____ tree

Name_____

Date_____

Directions: Write <u>Yes</u> if the boldfaced word serves as an adjective; write <u>No</u> if the boldfaced word does not serve as an adjective.

Remember: If a word serves as an adjective, it will modify (go over to) another word.

Examples: <u>Yes</u> Go out the **back** door. *Back what? Back door!*

<u>No</u> She has a sunburn on her **back**.

1. _____ The **taxi** driver smiled.

2. _____ We waited for a **taxi**.

3. _____ His mother likes to go to **yard** sales.

4. _____ Their front **yard** is large.

5. _____ Does he put **salt** on grapefruit?

6. _____ Please pass the **salt** shaker.

7. _____ Most children enjoy a **water** slide.

8. _____ He added **water** to a vase.

9. _____ Laura sleeps on her **stomach** most of the time.

10. _____ Do you have a **stomach** ache?

11. _____ A rabbit nibbled a small **berry**.

12. _____ Bill and Betty made a **berry** pie.

13. _____ A cook added oil and **garlic** to the frying pan.

14. _____ They love **garlic** bread.

PROPER ADJECTIVES

Proper adjectives come from proper nouns. A proper noun names a specific person, place, or thing.

	Examples:	common noun	proper noun
		lake	Lake Elsinore
		country	Switzerland

If we want to talk about tourists from Japan, we say **Japanese** tourists. *Japanese* is an adjective modifying (going over to) *tourists*. We do not say *Japan tourists*. We change the proper noun, *Japan*, to the adjective form, *Japanese*. Because the adjective form comes from a proper noun, we capitalize the word and refer to it as a proper adjective.

	Proper Noun	Proper Adjective	
Change:	Switzerland	Swiss	village
	China	Chinese	food
	Denmark	Danish	roll

Some proper nouns are the same in the proper adjective form.

Do not change:	Chewytime	Chewytime	gum
	Idaho	Idaho	potatoes

Name_____

Date_____

A. Directions: Write the proper adjective form and a noun it can modify.
     Example: Germany - <u>German forest</u>

1. America - _____   4. Arabia - _____

2. Texas - _____   5. Mooby - _____

3. Sweden - _____   6. Mexico - _____

B. Directions: Write the proper adjective and the noun it modifies in the space.
     Capitalize the proper adjective in the sentence.
                                    C
     Example: We saw a canadian wild goose.   <u>Canadian (wild) goose</u>

1. Do you like french bread? _____

2. He raised a united states flag. _____

3. Layla ate a swiss cheese sandwich. _____

4. They fished in an alaskan stream. _____

5. The farmer bought a deerwester tractor. _____

6. Ira asked about an african tour. _____

7. First graders are learning the spanish language. _____

8. Rafe loves his paterno stereo. _____

9. Salad was served with italian dressing. _____

10. She traveled on a nebraska freeway. _____

11. Do you like mississippi mud pie? _____

100

Name_____ **ADJECTIVES**
                                Identification
Date_____

Directions: Circle any adjectives.

Suggestion: First, identify any limiting adjectives. Then, reread the sentence and
             look for descriptive adjectives.

 1. Palm trees line that busy street.

 2. Several ducks waddled down a trail.

 3. She bought red glossy lipstick.

 4. Many playful dolphins swam in the ocean.

 5. We drank an orange drink with ice cubes.

 6. His younger sister has two mice.

 7. He purchased a few new wool sweaters.

 8. Do you want ice cream and a piece of peach pie?

 9. This chocolate cake requires no eggs.

10. A blue suede jacket was given to my friend.

11. The lady, tall and pretty, was once a famous model.

12. These potato chips don't have any salt.

13. Our favorite vacation place is near a hot spring.

14. The laughing baby rolled her big brown eyes.

15. I bought a round coffee table and some oak chairs at garage sales.

Degrees of Adjectives

Adjectives can make comparisons.

    A. The **comparative form** compares **two**.

    B. The **superlative form** compares **three or more**.

There are several ways to form the comparative and superlative forms:

    A. **Comparative**:

        1. Add **er** to most one-syllable adjectives:

            dull/duller   bold/bolder

        2. Add **er** to some two-syllable adjectives:

            creamy/creamier   dusty/dustier

        3. Place **more** (or less) before some two-syllable adjectives:

            faithful/more faithful   likable/more likable

IMPORTANT: Use a dictionary to determine if <u>er</u> should be added to a two-syllable adjective.

        4. Before adjectives of three or more syllables, add **more** (or less) to make comparisons.

            exciting/more exciting   embarrassed/more embarrassed

        5. Some adjectives completely change form.

            good/better   bad/worse

    B. **Superlative**:

        1. Add **est** to most one-syllable adjectives:

            dull/dullest   bold/boldest

        2. Add **est** to some two-syllable adjectives:

            creamy/creamiest   dusty/dustiest

        3. Place **most** (or least) before some two-syllable adjectives:

            faithful/most faithful   likable/most likable

Important: Use a dictionary to determine if <u>est</u> should be added to a two-syllable adjective.

        4. Place **most** (or least) before three-syllable adjectives.

            exciting/most exciting   embarrassed/most embarrassed

        5. Some adjectives totally change form.

            good/best   bad/worst

Name_____

Date_____

Directions: Write the adjective form in the space provided.

        Example: superlative of friendly -   _____friendliest_____

1.   comparative form of old - _____

2.   superlative form of old - _____

3.   comparative form of happy - _____

4.   superlative form of happy - _____

5.   comparative form of cheerful - _____

6.   superlative form of cheerful - _____

7.   comparative form of merry - _____

8.   superlative form of merry - _____

9.   comparative form of good - _____

10.   superlative form of good - _____

11.   comparative form of excited - _____

12.   comparative form of lovable - _____

13.   superlative form of cute - _____

14.   comparative form of lively - _____

15.   superlative form of dangerous - _____

Name_____   **ADJECTIVES**
                                       Degrees
Date_____

Directions: Circle the correct answer.

1. Jody is (taller, tallest) than Crissy.

2. My left foot is (longer, longest) than my right one.

3. This purse is (larger, largest) than that one.

4. Of the three apartments, the first one is (smaller, smallest).

5. Marge's dad is the (funnier, funniest) one of their family.

6. Shelley is the (older, oldest) twin.

7. That is the (more unusual, most unusual) painting in the museum.

8. Brittany's was the (faster, fastest) car in the race.

9. He is the (more active, most active) triplet.

10. Your story sounds (more believable, most believable) than his.

11. She is the (louder, loudest) cheerleader on the squad.

12. We were (more excited, most excited) the third time we rode the roller coaster.

13. The bride was (more exhausted, most exhausted) after the rehearsal than after the wedding.

14. Mark's aunt is (older, oldest) than his uncle.

15. Of the four trucks, the green one is (shinier, shiniest).

104

Name_____   **Adjective Review**

Date_____

A. Limiting Adjectives:

Directions: Fill in the blanks.

1. The three articles that serve as limiting adjectives are _____, _____, and _____.

2. The four demonstrative adjectives are _____, _____, _____, and _____.

3. Write a sentence with a number serving as an adjective: _____

_____

4. The possessive pronouns that can serve as adjectives are _____, _____,

_____, _____, _____, _____, _____, and _____.

5. Write your name + **'s** and something you own. _____

6. Three indefinites that can serve as adjectives are _____, _____,

and _____.

B. Adjective?:

Directions: Write <u>Yes</u> if the boldfaced word serves as an adjective. Write <u>No</u> if
the boldfaced word does not serve as an adjective.

1. _____   May I have **some**?

2. _____   May I have **some** peas, please.

3. _____   The **gas** tank in their car is quite large.

4. _____   Must we put **gas** in that lawn mower?

5. _____   Write your signature on the **line**.

6. _____   Their entire family likes to **line** dance.

Date_____

C. **Adjective Identification:**

Directions: Circle any adjective.

Suggestion: First, look for limiting adjectives. Then, reread the sentence searching
for descriptive adjectives.

1. One famous athlete spoke to a small middle school.

2. After the hockey game, several players ate a large meal.

3. Does your uncle drive an old black truck with shiny chrome wheels?

4. No fishing bait is sold at that general store.

5. His best friend sends him unusual baseball cards.

D. **Proper Adjectives:**

Directions: Capitalize any proper adjective.

1. Dad likes vermont maple syrup on his pancakes.

2. Rod likes to go to indianapolis races.

3. The first american flag may have been made by Betsy Ross.

4. Have your ever seen a south american monkey?

E. **Degrees of Adjectives:**

Directions: Circle the correct answer.

1. Jan is the (happier, happiest) student in the class.

2. Mitchell is (taller, tallest) than his mother.

3. Of the four kittens, Fluffy is the (more playful, most playful).

4. The second play was (gooder, better) than the first one.

5. Rattlesnakes are (more dangerous, most dangerous) than garter snakes.

A. **Object of the Preposition:**

   Directions: Cross out any prepositional phrases. Label the object of the
                preposition - O.P.

1. We dipped chips into a salsa.

2. Waves crashed against rocks on the shore.

🍓🍓🍓🍓🍓🍓🍓🍓🍓🍓🍓🍓🍓🍓🍓🍓🍓🍓🍓🍓🍓🍓🍓🍓🍓🍓🍓🍓🍓🍓🍓🍓🍓🍓🍓

B. **Prepositions:**

   Directions: Cross out any prepositional phrases. Underline the subject once
                and the verb/verb phrase twice. Label any direct object - D.O.

1. The class must leave within ten minutes.

2. He often sits under a tree during the evening.

3. Briana lives about five miles from her grandparents.

4. The family plants corn in their garden each year.

🍓🍓🍓🍓🍓🍓🍓🍓🍓🍓🍓🍓🍓🍓🍓🍓🍓🍓🍓🍓🍓🍓🍓🍓🍓🍓🍓🍓🍓🍓🍓🍓🍓🍓🍓

C. **Compound Subject:**

   Directions: Cross out any prepositional phrases. Underline the subject once
                and the verb/verb phrase twice.

Remember: Compound means more than one.

1. The coach and players practiced during the evening.

2. Her address and telephone number have been changed.

🍓🍓🍓🍓🍓🍓🍓🍓🍓🍓🍓🍓🍓🍓🍓🍓🍓🍓🍓🍓🍓🍓🍓🍓🍓🍓🍓🍓🍓🍓🍓🍓🍓🍓🍓

D. **Imperative Sentences:**

   Directions: Cross out any prepositional phrases. Underline the subject once
                and the verb/verb phrase twice.

1. Sit in that chair, please.

2. Call me after dinner.

E. Compound Objects of the Preposition:

Directions: Cross out any prepositional phrases. Underline the subject once and the verb/verb phrase twice.

1. A parachute consists of a canopy and a harness.

2. A scientist poured mixtures from a beaker and a test tube.

F. Compound Verbs:

Directions: Cross out any prepositional phrases. Underline the subject once and the verb/verb phrase twice.

1. The minister smiled and told a story about Joseph.

2. A bird flutters around the tree and flies through its branches.

G. Infinitives:

Directions: Cross out any prepositional phrases. Underline the subject once and the verb twice. Place an infinitive in parentheses ( ).

1. His family likes to ski in Colorado during January.

2. Do you want to bake a cake for Tony's birthday?

H. Contractions:

Directions: Write the contraction in the space provided.

1. I have - _____   5. you will - _____

2. where is - _____   6. I am - _____

3. they are - _____   7. might not - _____

4. could not - _____   8. are not - _____

I. **Action Verb?:**

Directions: Write <u>Yes</u> if the boldfaced verb shows action; write <u>No</u> if the boldfaced verb does not show action.

1. _____   Brandon **dropped** a quarter into the machine.

2. _____   The lady **nodded** her head in approval.

3. _____   Ms. Dean **seems** frustrated today.

J. **Regular or Irregular:**

Directions: Write <u>RV</u> if the verb is regular. Write <u>IV</u> if the verb is irregular.

Remember: Regular verbs add <u>ed</u> to the past and past participle.

1. _____   to bring   3. _____   to write   5. _____   to wash

2. _____   to follow   4. _____   to do   6. _____   to cook

K. **Tenses:**

Directions: Cross out any prepositional phrases. Underline the subject once and the verb/verb phrase twice. Write the tense on the line.

Remember: The tenses that we have learned are ***present***, ***past***, and ***future***.

1. _____   I shall talk with you later.

2. _____   Most people feed pigeons at that park.

3. _____   Two children danced in the talent show.

4. _____   Their family camps during the summer.

5. _____   Kari will arrive after her soccer game.

L. <u>Irregular Verbs:</u>

Directions: Circle the correct verb.

1. Have you (brung, brought) money with you?

2. He may have (took, taken) the shuttle to the airport.

3. I must have (run, ran) two miles.

4. Paul has (drank, drunk) several bottles of cola.

5. He should have (come, came) to the game at nine o'clock.

6. A child (lay, laid) on the floor with his dogs.

M. **Subject-Verb Agreement:**

Directions: Circle the verb that agrees with the subject.

1. Kriss Kringle (is, are) the British name for Santa Claus.

2. Several servers (leaves, leave) early each day.

3. One of the ladies (give, gives) many items to charity.

4. Kevin and his sister (travels, travel) to Alabama every summer.

N. **Concrete and Abstract Nouns:**

Directions: Write <u>C</u> if the noun is concrete; write <u>A</u> if the noun is abstract.

1. _____ lizard   3. _____ mask   5. _____ smoke

2. _____ truth   4. _____ money   6. _____ friendship

O. **Common and Proper Nouns:**

Directions: Write <u>CN</u> if the noun is common; write <u>PN</u> if the noun is proper.

1. _____ WOMAN   3. _____ VERMONT   5. _____ KITE

2. _____ APRICOT   4. _____ ST. LOUIS   6. _____ SPAIN

P. **Noun Identification:**

   Directions: Underline any nouns in each sentence.

Remember: You may wish to circle determiners to help you find most nouns.

1. Charlie's father became a pilot in the Navy.

2. That can of sweet potatoes is behind two bags of beans.

3. Those pictures of your trip to Oregon are beautiful.

Q. **Singular and Plural Nouns:**

   Directions: Write the plural.

1. key - _____   5. ox - _____

2. glass - _____   6. bubble - _____

3. wife - _____   7. bank - _____

4. tomato - _____   8. father-in-law - _____

R. **Possessive Nouns:**

   Directions: Write the possessive form.

1. a boat belonging to Melissa

   _____

2. a bus shared by many tourists

   _____

3. a company owned by more than one man

   _____

4. ferrets belonging to Chris

   _____

S. **Sentence Types:**

Directions: Write the sentence type in the space provided.

Remember: The four sentence types are declarative, interrogative, imperative, and exclamatory.

1. _____   Tie your shoe.

2. _____   You need an extra zero in that number.

3. _____   What is your phone number?

4. _____   The judge asked the witness to step down.

5. _____   We're here!

6. _____   Please wait your turn.

T. **Conjunctions:**

Directions: Circle any conjunctions.

1. I'll order a hamburger or hot dog.

2. A nurse and doctor entered the patient's room.

3. Mary and Sam's family is large, but everyone is always home for dinner.

U. **Interjections:**

Directions: Circle any interjections.

1. No!   The car won't start!

2. Whew! We made it!

3. This meat smells rotten! Yuck!

Adverbs tell *how*.

Most adverbs that tell *how* **go over to (modify) a verb.**

Most adverbs end in <u>ly</u>.

Example: <u>Do</u> that quickly!

Quickly tells *how* you should **do** that.

Crossing out prepositional phrases will help simplify the sentence. It will help you to find an adverb easily.

He stood quietly for ten minutes.

He <u>stood</u> quietly ~~for ten minutes~~.

Quietly tells *how* he stood.

Some adverbs that tell *how* are listed here. There are many more!

quickly	**carefully**	**quietly**
slowly	**happily**	**angrily**
sadly	**sincerely**	**helpfully**
fast	**hard**	**well**

Name_____

Date_____

Directions: Fill in the blanks.

　　　Example: She rocked the baby gently.

　　　　　　　Gently tells ___**how**___ she ___**rocked the baby**___.

1. The cook stirred the soup vigorously.

　　　Vigorously tells _____ the cook _____.

2. A child squirmed restlessly in his seat.

　　　Restlessly tells _____ the child _____.

3. Thunder boomed loudly around us.

　　　Loudly tells _____ the thunder _____.

4. A witness explained the robbery carefully.

　　　Carefully tells _____ the witness _____.

5. Several cloggers danced well.

　　　Well tells _____ the cloggers _____.

6. All of the travelers arrived safely.

　　　Safely tells _____ the travelers _____.

7. A boat sailed smoothly out to sea.

　　　Smoothly tells _____ a boat _____.

114

Directions: Circle the adverb that tells *how* in the following sentences. Draw an arrow to the verb it goes over to (modifies).

Note: **Crossing out prepositional phrases helps to find adverbs.**

1. He spoke loudly.

2. Jennipher smiled brightly.

3. The batter hit the ball hard.

4. We work together.

5. The frog jumped high.

6. Aunt Joy carefully planted a tree.

7. The ice cream man did his job cheerfully.

8. A rabbit hopped quickly down the dusty path.

9. That tennis player chuckles softly during each game.

10. The skier slid dangerously across the finish line.

Adverbs

Often a word has a noun form, an adjective form, and an adverb form.

Examples:	noun	adjective	adverb
	happiness	happy	happily
	creativity	creative	creatively
	laughter	laughing	laughingly
	intelligence	intelligent	intelligently

An adjective, as you have learned, describes a noun.

Mandy is a **soft** speaker.

Soft is an adjective that describes speaker.

The adverb form of *soft* is **softly**.

Incorrect: Mandy speaks soft.

Correct: Mandy speaks **softly**.

Softly is an adverb that tells HOW Mandy speaks.

🍓🍓🍓🍓🍓🍓🍓🍓🍓🍓🍓🍓🍓🍓🍓🍓🍓🍓🍓🍓🍓🍓🍓🍓🍓🍓🍓🍓🍓🍓🍓🍓🍓

There are two exceptions to this that you will frequently encounter: *fast* and *hard*.

Fast is the same in both the adjective form and adverb form:

Patty and Austin are *fast* runners.   (adjective describing runners)
Patty and Austin run *fast*.   (adverb telling how)

Hard is the same in both the adjective form and adverb form:

My mother is a *hard* hitter.   (adjective describing hitter)
My mother hits a baseball *hard*.   (adverb telling how)

Many adverb tell *how*.   Adverbs that tell *how* usually modify (go over to) a verb.

Most adverbs that tell *how* end in **ly**.

Frequently, the adverb form is similar to the adjective form.

> Remember, adjectives modify nouns (or pronouns).

> Example: That is a dangerous road.   *Dangerous* is an adjective describing road.

>> adjective - dangerous   adverb - dangerously

> Example: Some people drive dangerously on that road.

>> *Dangerously* tells **how** some people drive.

Directions: Write the adverb form of each adjective.

	ADJECTIVE	**ADVERB**
1.	sad	_____
2.	loving	_____
3.	patient	_____
4.	slow	_____
5.	sincere	_____
6.	quick	_____
7.	grump	_____
8.	cheerful	_____
9.	fast	_____

Name_____   **ADVERBS**
                                              How?

Date_____

Many adverb tell **how**.   Adverbs that tell **how** usually modify (go over to) a verb.

> Examples: Marilyn draws *carefully.*
>
> > *Carefully* tells how she <u>draws</u>.
>
> > A police officer motioned *vigorously* to the motorists.
>
> > *Vigorously* tells how the officer <u>motioned</u>.
>
> > They run *fast.*
>
> > *Fast* tells how they <u>run</u>.

Most adverbs that tell **how** end in **ly**.

🍓🍓🍓🍓🍓🍓🍓🍓🍓🍓🍓🍓🍓🍓🍓🍓🍓🍓🍓🍓🍓🍓🍓🍓🍓🍓🍓🍓🍓🍓🍓🍓🍓🍓🍓🍓🍓🍓

Directions: Fill in the blanks.

> Example: They talked quietly. *Quietly* tells ___**how**___ they ___**talked**___.

1. The cat purred softly. *Softly* tells _____the cat _____.

2. The soldiers ate hungrily. *Hungrily* tells _____ the soldiers _____.

3. Grandma laughed happily as she opened her present. *Happily* tells _____

    Grandma _____.

4. The small boy looked tearfully at his father. *Tearfully* tells _____ the boy

    _____.

5. The man answered sternly. *Sternly* tells _____the man _____.

6. An electrician worked hard all afternoon. *Hard* tells _____the electrician

    _____.

It is important to use the correct form in our speaking and writing.

The following sentence is incorrect.   **Joel skates slow.**

Joel is a slow skater.   *Slow* is an adjective that modifies the noun, <u>skater</u>.

Since *slow* is an adjective, it cannot tell *how* Joel skates.

Correct: Joel skates slowly.

There are several words that are the same in both adjective and adverb forms.

Examples: hard   He is a hard hitter.   He hits the ball hard.

fast   I am a fast walker.   I walk fast.

However, **most words do change**.   Use a **dictionary** to determine the adverb form. For <u>slow</u>, it will say *adv.* <u>slowly</u>.   Often the adverb listing is in boldfaced print.

🍓🍓🍓🍓🍓🍓🍓🍓🍓🍓🍓🍓🍓🍓🍓🍓🍓🍓🍓🍓🍓🍓🍓🍓🍓🍓🍓🍓🍓🍓🍓🍓🍓🍓🍓🍓🍓🍓🍓

Directions: Fill in the blank with the adverb form of the word in parenthesis.

Example: (cheerful)   He always speaks __<u>cheerfully</u>__ to us.

1.   (proper)   Sit _____, please.

2.   (frequent)   That lady flies _____.

3.   (rude)   Please don't speak _____ to me.

4.   (timid)   The speaker replied _____.

5.   (forceful)   A falling skater hit the pavement _____.

6.   (tight)   The child hugged his teddy bear _____.

7.   (firm)   The senator responded _____.

8.   (skillful)   A craftsman _____ carved a statue.

Adverbs tell _when_.

Most adverbs that tell _when_ **usually go over to (modify) a verb.**

Example: They <u>left</u> **yesterday.**

Yesterday tells when they **left.**

Some adverbs that tell _when_ are listed here:

now	**when**	**always**
then	**whenever**	**daily**
soon	**first**	**sometimes**
sooner	**afterwards**	**yesterday**
late	**never**	**today**
later	**forever**	**tomorrow**

Examples:

First, the telephone rang.   When? first

Then, the lady answered it.   When? then

She **never** turns on the answering machine.   When? never

120

A. Directions: Unscramble these adverbs that tell **when**.

1. tela - _____   10. own - _____

2. hewn - _____   11. roromotw - _____

3. noso - _____   12. tirsf - _____

4. neth - _____   13. retal - _____

5. doyta - _____   14. vehnewre - _____

6. ernoos - _____   15. adyil - _____

7. renev - _____   16. yawals - _____

8. stayderye - _____   17. netof - _____

9. mimessote - _____   18. drawsteafr - _____

B. Directions: Write the adverb that tells *when* in the space provided.

1. antonym (opposite) for *late* - _____

2. by the hour - _____

3. synonym (same) for *tardy* -_____

4. every day - _____

5. at all times - _____

Directions: Circle the adverb that tells *when* in the following sentences. Draw an arrow to the verb it goes over to (modifies).

Note: Crossing out prepositional phrases helps to find adverbs.

1. He wants an answer now.

2. That clerk never leaves before dinner.

3. A barbecue will be held tonight.

4. The guide arrived early in the morning.

5. His leader seldom arrives on time.

6. She immediately looked around the room.

7. The student sometimes walks to school.

8. Some fishermen always take a net.

9. That golfer frequently uses pink golf balls.

10. Her grandfather will visit today.

Adverbs tell *where*.

Adverbs that tell *where* **usually go over to (modify) a verb.**

Example: I looked everywhere for our dog.

Everywhere tells *where* I looked.

Some adverbs that tell *where* are listed here:

here	anywhere	in	up
there	somewhere	out	down
where	everywhere	inside	near
nowhere	home	outside	far

Examples:

Let's go **inside**.   Where?   inside

Sam went **home** ~~for lunch~~.   Where?   home

🍓 Did you notice that some words that you learned as prepositions are on the list? They serve as adverbs only when they aren't in a prepositional phrase.

Examples: Kelly went **inside**.   (adverb)

Gregg hid **~~inside the front door~~**.   (preposition)

She ran **~~up the hill~~**.   (preposition)

She looked **up**.   (adverb)

Name_____   **ADVERBS**
                                              Where?
Date_____

A. Directions: Unscramble these adverbs that tell ***where***.

    1. pu - _____   6. ownd - _____

    2. eerh - _____   7. veywehreer - _____

    3. emoh - _____   8. raf - _____

    4. hrtee - _____   9. setudoi - _____

    5. tou- _____   10. hewre - _____

B. Directions: Write the adverb that tells *where* in the space provided.

1. antonym (opposite) for *far* - _____

2. antonym (opposite) for *outside* - _____

3. where you live -_____

C. Directions: Write any adverb that ends with *ere*.

1. _____   5. _____

2. _____   6. _____

3. _____   7. _____

4. _____

124

Directions: Circle the adverb that tells *where* in the following sentences. Draw an arrow to the verb it goes over to (modifies).

Note: Crossing out prepositional phrases helps to find adverbs.

1. The child fell down.

2. Mark visited there last winter.

3. Where may I sit?

4. He walked far.

5. I searched everywhere for my wallet.

6. They played outside.

7. Their sister lives nearby.

8. You may come in.

9. Chad went somewhere with his mother.

10. Mary stays here during the summer.

Adverbs

Adverbs are one-word modifiers. In other words, *down the road* tells **where**, but it is not an adverb.

Examples: Stay **here**, please.

Do you live **nearby**?

🍓🍓🍓🍓🍓🍓🍓🍓🍓🍓🍓🍓🍓🍓🍓🍓🍓🍓🍓🍓🍓🍓🍓🍓🍓🍓🍓🍓🍓🍓🍓🍓🍓🍓

You have learned the following words as prepositions:

across	inside	over
along	near	past
around	on	through
down	out	under
in	outside	up

These words are prepositions when they are followed by a noun (or pronoun).

The team went ~~inside the dugout~~.   (inside = preposition)

Inside the dugout is a prepositional phrase.

These same words serve as adverbs when they are not followed by a noun (or pronoun).

After lunch, the class went **inside**.   (inside = adverb)

Inside tells *where* the class went.

Name_____   **ADVERBS**
                                          Where?

Date_____

A. Directions: Write <u>Prep.</u> if the boldfaced word serves as a preposition.
                 Write <u>Adv.</u> if the boldfaced word serves as an adverb that tells where.

            Examples: <u>Adv.</u>   Come **along**.

                          <u>Prep.</u>   A horse trotted **along** a wooded trail.

1. _____   Chet fell **over** a chair.

2. _____   A broom fell **over**.

3. _____   The skater looked **down**.

4. _____   Mr. Ripple walks **down** the lane daily.

5. _____   She searched **through** the drawer for a sock.

6. _____   Do you need to come **through** here?

7. _____   The dog looked **around** and trotted off.

8. _____   That lady and her daughter walk **around** the block each evening.

B. Directions: Write a sentence, using the boldfaced word as an adverb.
                 Then, write a sentence, using the boldfaced word as a preposition.

1. **up**

        (adverb)   _____

        (preposition) _____

2. **outside**

        (adverb)   _____

        (preposition) _____

Adverbs

To What Extent?

Seven adverbs are used frequently in our language to tell *to what extent*. They are **not**, **so**, **very**, **too**, **quite**, **rather**, and **somewhat**. When you see these in a sentence, they will be adverbs.

Examples:　He is *not* sick.

　　　　　He is *so* sick.

　　　　　He is *very* sick.

　　　　　He is *too* sick to go anywhere.

　　　　　He is *quite* sick.

　　　　　He is *rather* sick.

　　　　　He is *somewhat* sick.

These adverbs tell to what extent the person is sick. As you know, there is a great difference between being somewhat sick and so sick. Adverbs such as *somewhat* and *so* tell *to what extent*.

🍓🍓🍓🍓🍓🍓🍓🍓🍓🍓🍓🍓🍓🍓🍓🍓🍓🍓🍓🍓🍓🍓🍓🍓🍓🍓🍓🍓🍓🍓🍓🍓🍓🍓🍓🍓

There are other adverbs that tell *to what extent*.

Examples:　That weight lifter has an **unusually** large appetite.

　　　　　(To what extent large?　　unusually large)

　　　　　Her sister is **extremely** funny.

　　　　　(To what extent funny?　　extremely funny)

128

Directions: Circle any adverb that tells *to what extent* in the following sentences.

1. Beef was not served for lunch.

2. The dog groomer is so busy today.

3. An elephant is a very heavy animal.

4. This chocolate pudding is too watery.

5. That child was quite sick last week.

6. An oarfish has a rather long body.

7. His somewhat silly answer made us laugh.

8. Their minister is extremely kind.

9. Toby's finger swelled to an unusually large size.

10. My best friend is too stubborn.

11. I would rather not disturb my sleeping cat.

12. Bruce is somewhat shy, but his brother is so talkative.

13. The dentist examined her teeth extremely well.

14. He's quite tall and very strong.

15. Isn't a paca a tropical rodent?

Degrees of Adverbs

Adverbs can be used to compare:

A. Sometimes, two *things* are compared.

   Example: This car goes faster than that truck.

   **Here we are comparing two items, a car and a truck.
   Faster is a form of *fast* which tells <u>HOW</u> they run.**

   When two items are compared, the **comparative** form is used.
   There are three ways to form the comparative:

   1. Add <u>er</u> to most one-syllable adverbs.

      soon - sooner

   2. Place <u>more</u> before most two or more syllable adverbs.

      recently - more recently

   Some two syllable adverbs add <u>er</u>.

   early - earlier

Use a dictionary to help you decide the adverb form.

   Here is the entry for the adverb, <u>early</u>:

   early, *adv.* **-lier**, liest

If <u>more</u> should be used, no <u>er</u> form will be given in the dictionary.

   3. Some adverbs totally change form.

well - better

B.   Sometimes, three or more *things* are compared.

Example: She runs fastest of the entire team.

There are three ways to form the superlative:

1.   Add **est** to most one-syllable adverbs.

hard/hardest

2.   Place **most** before many two or more syllable adverbs.

slowly/most slowly

Use a dictionary to help you decide the adverb form.

Here is the entry for the adverb, <u>early</u>:

early, *adv.* -lier, **liest**

If <u>most</u> should be used, no <u>est</u> form will be given in the dictionary.

3.   Some adverbs totally change form.

well/best

Adverb	**Comparative**	**Superlative**
happily	more happily	most happily
late	later	latest
well	better	best

131

Name_____   **ADVERBS**
                                        Degrees of Adverbs
Date_____

A. Directions: Finish the sentence with the correct word.

1. a. Jeremy hits the ball far.

    b. However, his sister hits the ball _____.

2. a. Mrs. Bream talks softly.

    b. However, her friend talks _____.

3. a. Our neighbor cuts her lawn early in the morning.

    b. Her husband cuts it _____ than she does.

4. a. Ginger drives very carefully.

    b. Her grandmother, however, drives even _____
        than Ginger.

B. Directions: Circle the correct answer.

1. The white top spins (faster, fastest) than the yellow one.

2. Mrs. King spoke (more pleasantly, most pleasantly) to the teacher than to her
    misbehaving son.

3. The wind blew (more violently, most violently) the third day of the hurricane.

4. Justin sanded the wooden toy (more rapidly, most rapidly) during the fourth
    sanding.

5. She fell (harder, hardest) the second time she tried to mount the horse.

6. He hit the golf ball (more powerfully, most powerfully) on his fifth try.

Name_____   **ADVERBS**
                                              Degrees of Adverbs
Date_____

A. Directions: Finish the sentence with the correct word.

1. a.   Mika climbed high into the tree.

    b.   However, her sister climbed _____.

2. a.   Alvah arrived late.

    b.   However, Marcos arrived _____.

3. a.   Amber skates smoothly.

    b.   Her best friend skates _____ than Amber.

B. Directions: Circle the correct answer.

1. The red ball was hit (harder, hardest) than the blue one.

2. Of the two, Carlo whistles (more softly, most softly).

3. William asks (more politely, most politely) of all the boys.

4. My brother runs (faster, fastest) of his entire soccer team.

5. She signed her name (more carefully, most carefully) on the second paper.

6. Lulu's dad swims (more slowly, most slowly) on his tenth lap.

7. The fourth batch of cookies turned out (better, best).

8. Ken holds a bat (more tightly, most tightly) than his friend.

Double Negatives

No, not, never, none, no one, nobody, nothing, scarcely, and hardly
are called *negative words*. <u>Do not use more than one negative word in the same</u> <u>sentence</u>.

Example: Wrong: I am **not** doing **nothing**.

           Right: I am **not** doing anything.

OR

I am doing **nothing**.

           Wrong: Erma **never** goes **nowhere**.

           Right: Erma **never** goes anywhere.

OR

Erma goes **nowhere**.

However, if *no* is used to answer a question, another negative word may be used in the sentence.

Are you allowed to go?

No, I am **not** allowed to go.

🍓🍓🍓🍓🍓🍓🍓🍓🍓🍓🍓🍓🍓🍓🍓🍓🍓🍓🍓🍓🍓🍓🍓🍓🍓🍓🍓🍓🍓🍓🍓🍓🍓🍓🍓🍓🍓

If you have been around anyone who uses double negatives, the incorrect usage may "sound" right. Always check to see if two of the words on your double negative list are in the same sentence.

No, *not*, *never*, *none*, *no one*, *nobody*, *nothing*, *scarcely*, and *hardly* are negative words.

A. Directions: Circle the negative word in each sentence.

1. She never bites her nails.

2. The tile has no wax on it.

3. Nothing happened.

4. He could scarcely talk.

5. I want none, thanks.

6. They hardly had time to finish.

7. We saw nobody that we knew.

B. Directions: Write the sentence correctly.

1. This bottle doesn't have no lid.

_____

2. They would not carry nothing to the car.

_____

3. He hardly has no clean socks.

_____

4. You never talk to nobody.

_____

No, *not*, *never*, *none*, *no one*, *nobody*, *nothing*, *scarcely*, and *hardly* are negative words.

A. Directions: Write the sentence correctly.

1. The fisherman hadn't caught nothing.

_____

2. I don't have none.

_____

3. We never get no popsicles for lunch.

_____

B. Directions: Circle the correct word.

1. He won't take (nobody, anybody) with him.

2. Our dog never has (any, no) bones.

3. No one wants (anything, nothing) to eat yet.

4. She hardly (never, ever) sits by the fire.

5. Mom doesn't have (no, any) dimes or quarters.

6. Harvey scarcely has (anything, nothing) to do.

7. Lois has not written to (any, none) of her relatives.

8. Joe doesn't want (nobody, anybody) to help him.

A. **Adverbs:**

Directions: Write the adverb form of the word.

1. brave - _____   4. exact - _____

2. excited - _____   5. stupid - _____

3. happy - _____   6. furious - _____

B. **How?:**

Directions: Circle any adverbs that tell *how*.

1. Please look carefully before crossing the street.

2. Sue talks constantly about her new cat.

3. A six-year-old hit the ball and ran fast to first base.

4. The teenager listened silently as his father spoke.

C. **How?:**

Directions: Write the adverb form for the boldfaced word.

1. Brandy has a **loud** voice. Brandy speaks _____.

2. That stewardess is a **polite** woman. She treats all of the passengers

_____.

3. Their friend has a **strange** laugh. She laughs _____.

4. Ned is a **fast** typist. He types _____.

Name_____

Date_____

D. **Where?:**

    Directions: Circle any adverbs that tell *where*.

1. Where are you going?

2. Let's go somewhere to talk.

3. He stooped down and looked up.

4. The salesmen went downtown for a meeting.

E. **Adverb or Preposition?:**

    Directions: Write <u>Prep</u>. if the boldfaced word serves as a preposition.
                    Write <u>Adv</u>. if the boldfaced word serves as an adverb.

      Examples: __Adv.__   Marco came **over** ~~to my house~~.

1. _____   Do you live **near**?

2. _____   Do you live **near** a store?

3. _____   Our dog needs to go **out** for a walk.

4. _____   The dog ran **out** the open door.

F. **To What Extent?:**

    Directions: Circle any adverbs that tell *to what extent*.

1. You seem quite tired today.

2. Mr. and Mrs. Smith are very happy about their new twins.

3. She did not bowl so rapidly during her second game.

G. **Degrees of Adverbs:**

    Directions: Circle the correct adverb form.

1. Janell throws the ball (higher, highest) than Lisa.

2. Of the three race cars, the red one runs (faster, fastest).

3. The shortstop plays (more often, oftener) than the first base person.

4. That assistant performs (better, best) than her boss.

5. Cindy danced (more calmly, most calmly) during the second performance.

6. Of the three machines, the first one runs (more smoothly, most smoothly).

7. Do you ride your bike (more rapidly, most rapidly) than your brother?

8. Brett cleaned his room (more completely, most completely) the fourth time.

H. **Double Negatives:**

    Directions: Circle the correct answer.

1. Don't take (no, any) candy from a stranger.

2. Kim never has (nothing, anything) to do.

3. I don't want (any, none).

4. She doesn't want (anybody, nobody) to see her.

5. We shouldn't (never, ever) go swimming alone.

6. Kent hardly has (no, any) time for hobbies.

A. **Object of the Preposition:**

Directions: Cross out any prepositional phrases. Label the object of the
preposition - O.P.

1. We sat in the first row.

2. Before church, the family eats at a small diner.

🍓🍓🍓🍓🍓🍓🍓🍓🍓🍓🍓🍓🍓🍓🍓🍓🍓🍓🍓🍓🍓🍓🍓🍓🍓🍓🍓🍓🍓🍓🍓🍓🍓🍓

B. **Compound Object of the Preposition:**

Directions: Cross out any prepositional phrases. Label the object of the
preposition - O.P.

Remember: Compound means more than one.

1. We hiked with Toni and Andy.

2. A postal card from Grandma and Grandpa came today.

🍓🍓🍓🍓🍓🍓🍓🍓🍓🍓🍓🍓🍓🍓🍓🍓🍓🍓🍓🍓🍓🍓🍓🍓🍓🍓🍓🍓🍓🍓🍓🍓🍓🍓

C. **Compound Subject:**
Directions: Cross out any prepositional phrases. Underline the subject once
and the verb/verb phrase twice.

Remember: Compound means more than one.

1. Their dog and cat run through the house.

2. Before school, Cynthia and her mom went for a walk.

🍓🍓🍓🍓🍓🍓🍓🍓🍓🍓🍓🍓🍓🍓🍓🍓🍓🍓🍓🍓🍓🍓🍓🍓🍓🍓🍓🍓🍓🍓🍓🍓🍓🍓

D. **Imperative Sentences:**

Directions: Cross out any prepositional phrases. Underline the subject once
and the verb/verb phrase twice.

1. Put this into the cupboard.

2. Toss the water balloon to me.

E. **Compound Verbs:**

Directions: Cross out any prepositional phrases. Underline the subject once and the verb/verb phrase twice.

1. I always wash and wax floors in the morning.

2. Judd called my name and motioned toward me.

🍓🍓🍓🍓🍓🍓🍓🍓🍓🍓🍓🍓🍓🍓🍓🍓🍓🍓🍓🍓🍓🍓🍓🍓🍓🍓🍓🍓🍓🍓🍓

F. **Infinitives:**

Directions: Cross out any prepositional phrases. Underline the subject once and the verb twice. Place an infinitive in parenthesis (   ).

1. That lady likes to work at her computer.

2. After the flood, people came to help.

🍓🍓🍓🍓🍓🍓🍓🍓🍓🍓🍓🍓🍓🍓🍓🍓🍓🍓🍓🍓🍓🍓🍓🍓🍓🍓🍓🍓🍓🍓🍓

G. **Contractions:**

Directions: Write the contraction in the space provided.

1. do not - _____   7. they are - _____

2. you will - _____   8. where is - _____

3. you are - _____   9. have not - _____

4. will not - _____   10. we were - _____

5. had not - _____   11. cannot - _____

6. I shall - _____   12. she is - _____

🍓🍓🍓🍓🍓🍓🍓🍓🍓🍓🍓🍓🍓🍓🍓🍓🍓🍓🍓🍓🍓🍓🍓🍓🍓🍓🍓🍓🍓🍓🍓

H. **Action Verb?:**

Directions: Write <u>Yes</u> if the boldfaced verb shows action; write <u>No</u> if the boldfaced verb does not show action.

1. _____ He **climbed** a hill.   3. _____ You **seem** sad.

2. _____ I **eat** many bananas.   4. _____ The gong **sounds** loud.

I. **Regular or Irregular:**

   Directions: Write <u>RV</u> if the verb is regular. Write <u>IV</u> if the verb is irregular.

   Remember: Regular verbs add <u>ed</u> to the past and past participle.

1. _____ to love   3. _____ to bleed   5. _____ to change

2. _____ to give   4. _____ to break   6. _____ to steal

&&&&&&&&&&&&&&&&&&&&&&&&&&&&&&&&&&&&&&&&&&&

J. **Tenses:**

   Directions: Cross out any prepositional phrases. Underline the subject once
   and the verb/verb phrase twice. Write the tense on the line.

   Remember: The tenses that we have learned are *present*, *past*, and *future*.

1. _____   Mark will go to the beach in June.

2. _____   That scuba diver enjoys his hobby.

3. _____   They surfed for several hours.

&&&&&&&&&&&&&&&&&&&&&&&&&&&&&&&&&&&&&&&&&&&

K. **Subject-Verb Agreement:**

   Directions: Circle the verb that agrees with the subject.

1. Nina and Troy (sing, sings) in a choir.

2. Mrs. Dobbs (want, wants) to be an actress.

3. Those children (plays, play) well together.

&&&&&&&&&&&&&&&&&&&&&&&&&&&&&&&&&&&&&&&&&&&

L. **Irregular Verbs:**

   Directions: Write the past participle form.

1. to run - ____(had)_____   3. to go - ____(had)_____

2. to drink - ____(had)_____   4. to ride - ____(had)_____

M. **Irregular Verbs:**

   Directions: Cross out prepositional phrases. Underline the subject once and the verb phrase twice. **(Be sure to underline the helping verbs + the main verb in parenthesis.)**

1. We have not (ate, eaten) lunch.

2. Several funnel clouds were (see, seen).

3. Where has Steve (went, gone)?

4. The driver may have (come, came) for the packages.

5. Ted and Ike have (flew, flown) in a large jet.

6. Hannah had (laid, lain) by the pool before noon.

7. Marcia should have (gave, given) her dog a bath.

N. **Concrete and Abstract Nouns:**

   Directions: Write <u>C</u> if the noun is concrete; write <u>A</u> if the noun is abstract.

1. _____ friendship   2. _____ honey   3. _____ mop

O. **Common and Proper Nouns:**

   Directions: Write <u>CN</u> if the noun is common; write <u>PN</u> is the noun is proper.

1. _____ APPLE   2. _____ ALASKA   3. _____ RUG

P. **Noun Identification:**

   Directions: Underline any nouns in each sentence.

   Remember: You may wish to circle determiners to help you find most nouns.

1. Many cows grazed in a meadow near the large barn.

2. Two red roses in a glass vase had been placed on our dining table.   143

Name_____

Date_____

Q. **Singular and Plural Nouns:**
   Directions: Write the plural.

1. ray - _____

2. tomato - _____

3. mix - _____

4. train - _____

5. child - _____

6. sheep - _____

7. name - _____

8. dictionary - _____

R. **Possessive Nouns:**
   Directions: Write the possessive form.

1. a horse belonging to Heidi

   _____

2. marbles owned by several boys

   _____

3. a barn used for cows

   _____

S. **Sentence Types**
   Directions: Write the sentence type in the space provided.
   Remember: The four sentence types are declarative, interrogative, imperative,
   and exclamatory.

1. _____   My friend's mother is waxing her car.

2. _____   Do you like to play games?

3. _____   Wash your face.

4. _____   I've been selected for the all-star team!

144

T. **Conjunctions and Interjections:**

   Directions: Label any conjunction - CONJ.; label any interjection - INTJ.

1. Yikes! John and Mary forgot their luggage!

2. We want Chinese or Mexican food tonight.

🍓🍓🍓🍓🍓🍓🍓🍓🍓🍓🍓🍓🍓🍓🍓🍓🍓🍓🍓🍓🍓🍓🍓🍓🍓🍓🍓🍓🍓🍓🍓🍓🍓🍓🍓

U. **Adjective?:**

   Directions: Write <u>Yes</u> if the boldfaced word serves as an adjective. Write <u>No</u> if
   the boldfaced word does not serve as an adjective.

1. _____   Their **street** light is burned out.

2. _____   Several small trees were planted in a **field**.

3. _____   Have you ever seen a **field** mouse?

🍓🍓🍓🍓🍓🍓🍓🍓🍓🍓🍓🍓🍓🍓🍓🍓🍓🍓🍓🍓🍓🍓🍓🍓🍓🍓🍓🍓🍓🍓🍓🍓🍓🍓

V. **Degrees of Adjectives:**

   Directions: Circle the correct answer.

1. This Cajun chicken is (spicier, spiciest) than the barbecued chicken.

2. Of the three referees, she is the (fairer, fairest).

3. Lori is the (more creative, most creative) twin.

🍓🍓🍓🍓🍓🍓🍓🍓🍓🍓🍓🍓🍓🍓🍓🍓🍓🍓🍓🍓🍓🍓🍓🍓🍓🍓🍓🍓🍓🍓🍓🍓🍓🍓

W. **Adjective Identification:**

   Directions: Circle any adjectives.

Suggestion: First, look for limiting adjectives. Then, reread the sentence searching
   for descriptive adjectives.

1. A few bees have landed on the yellow flower.

2. Two new cars skidded on an icy street.

Name_____

Date_____

X. **Prepositions:**

Directions: List forty prepositions.

1. _____   21. _____
2. _____   22. _____
3. _____   23. _____
4. _____   24. _____
5. _____   25. _____
6. _____   26. _____
7. _____   27. _____
8. _____   28. _____
9. _____   29. _____
10. _____   30. _____
11. _____   31. _____
12. _____   32. _____
13. _____   33. _____
14. _____   34. _____
15. _____   35. _____
16. _____   36. _____
17. _____   37. _____
18. _____   38. _____
19. _____   39. _____
20. _____   40. _____

Y. **Helping Verbs:**

Directions: List the twenty-three helping verbs.

_____

_____

_____

146

PRONOUNS

Personal Pronouns

Pronouns take the place of nouns.

Nominative pronouns usually serve as the **subject** of a sentence. Nominative pronouns include **I**, **he**, **she**, **we**, **they**, **you**, **who**, and **it**.

Examples: **Mary** makes birdhouses.

She makes birdhouses.

Brett and Joe are selling popsicles.

They are selling popsicles.

Is **Mr. Dobbs** your friend?

Is **he** your friend?

Important: If you are talking about yourself, use the pronoun, **I,** at or near the beginning of a sentence.

Example: After lunch, **I** played with my friend.

When referring to yourself and another person, say the other person's name first.

Example: **Matt** and **I** bought ice cream.

🍓 🍓 🍓 **Do not say** Matt and me or me and Matt. 🍓 🍓 🍓

Name_____

Date_____

Directions: In part <u>A</u>, insert a person's name in the blank. In part <u>B</u>, use a pronoun to replace the person's name; in the double underlined part, finish the sentence.

Example: A.   _____Josh_____ is my brother.

B.   _____He_____ is__very nice to our dog.__

1. A. _____ is my friend.

B. _____ is_____

2. A. _____ is my teacher.

B. _____ is_____

3. A. _____ is a member of my family.

B. _____ is_____

4. A. _____ is an older person who is important to me.

B. _____ is_____

5. A. _____ is an animal.

B. _____ is_____

148

Name_____   **PRONOUNS**
                                    As Subject
Date_____

A.   Directions: On the line provided, write each sentence correctly.

1.   I and my friend want to stay.

     _____

2.   My dad and me are going.

     _____

3.   Me and Terry played at the park.

     _____

4.   Me and my friends aren't doing that.

     _____

B.   Directions: Write the correct pronoun on the line.

_____ 1.   (Me, I) want to go, too.

_____ 2.   (Her, She) is the winner!

_____ 3.   All afternoon (they, them) played in their yard.

_____ 4.   (We, Us) enjoy scary stories.

_____ 5.   Today, (he, him) is going to the zoo.

_____ 6.   May Mike and (me, I) help you?

PRONOUNS

Pronouns take the place of nouns.

Objective pronouns are usually used after a preposition or as a direct object. Objective pronouns include **me**, **him**, **her**, **us**, **them**, **you**, **whom**, and **it**.

Examples: The coach is talking to the **girl.**

                The coach is talking to **her.**   (object of the preposition)

                The ball hit **Jack** on the leg.

                The ball hit **him** on the leg.   (direct object)

Name_____

Date_____

A. Directions: Place an X above the preposition. Then, circle the correct pronoun.

   Remember: After a preposition, you will use an objective pronoun. Objective pronouns include *me*, *him*, *her*, *us*, *them*, *you*, and *it*.

1. Are you going with (we, us)?

2. I have given the bag to (him, he).

3. This is from (they, them).

4. The story is about (her, she).

5. Sit between John and (I, me).

B. Directions: In sentence A, underline the subject once and the verb twice. Label the direct object - D.O. In part B, insert a pronoun for the word(s) labeled as a direct object.

1. A. The team chose Jan.

   B. The team chose _____.

2. A. A rubber ball hit John.

   B. A rubber ball hit _____.

3. A. The lady dropped her wallet.

   B. The lady dropped _____.

4. A. Dad hugged Susie and Ryan.

   B. Dad hugged _____.

Directions: Write a pronoun for the boldfaced noun(s).

1. A.   The puppy followed _____.
                              (your name)

    B.   The puppy followed _____.

2. A.   A calendar was given to **Anne**.

    B.   A calendar was given to _____.

3. A.   The singer sang to **Brad and Carol**.

    B.   The singer sang to _____.

4. A.   A dog licked **Miss Post** for several seconds.

    B.   A dog licked _____ for several seconds.

5. A.   Their uncle went with **Shari and our family** to a baseball game.

    B.   Their uncle went with _____ to a baseball game.

6. A.   Mother handed the **bird** to her friend.

    B.   Mother handed _____ to her friend.

Name_____

Date_____

Directions: On the line provided, write each sentence correctly.

1. Do you want to eat lunch with I?

_____

2. Marsha lives near he.

_____

3. The artist talked to they about his painting.

_____

4. My friend gave I two pencils.

_____

5. Please give we your answer!

_____

6. This letter is from she.

_____

7. Their moms met they at a park.

_____

Compound Pronouns

Compound means more than one.

Sometimes, there is more than one subject of a sentence. This is called a **compound subject.**

> Example: <u>**Lela**</u> and <u>**Kissa**</u> chose several guppies.
>
> <u>**Lela**</u> and <u>**she**</u> chose several guppies.

Sometimes, there is more than one object in a sentence.

> Examples: An older girl sat beside **Kami** and **Kyle**.
>
> An older girl sat beside **Kami** and **him**.

Pronoun Finger Trick:

If you are unsure which pronoun to use, place your finger or fingers over the first part of the compound.

> Example: Lela and (her, she) chose several guppies.
>
> **Her** chose several guppies.   Incorrect!
>
> **She** chose several guppies.   Correct!
>
> Lela and (her, **she**) chose several guppies.

> Example: An older girl sat beside Kami and (he, him).
>
> An older girl sat beside   **he**.   Incorrect!
>
> An older girl sat beside   **him**.   Correct!
>
> An older girl sat beside Kami and (he, **him**).

154

Name_____

Date_____

Directions: Circle the correct pronoun.

Remember: Place your finger or fingers over the first part of the compound. Then, reread the sentence and choose the correct pronoun.

1. Pat and (me, I) decided to sell cookies during the summer.

2. Come with Jarred and (me, I).

3. The policeman and (they, them) talked for an hour.

4. Glenn didn't ask Sally or (I, me) to his party.

5. Dad and (him, he) often fish in that lake.

6. The coach sat near Bob and (she, her) on the bleachers.

7. Mrs. Winters and (her, she) often put puzzles together.

8. A box of colored chalk was given to Jody and (us, we).

9. Last week, his mother and (he, him) shopped for shoes.

10. The librarian and (us, we) searched for a good fiction book.

11. During the storm in the afternoon, the children and (they, them) rushed inside.

12. The gift from Spencer's brother and (we, us) needs to be wrapped.

Directions: Circle the correct pronoun.

Remember: Place your finger or fingers over the first part of the compound.   Then, reread the sentence and choose the correct pronoun.

1.   An invitation for Mandy and (she, her) came in the mail.

2.   Zek and (me, I) want to watch television.

3.   Have you asked your mother and (she, her) to help you?

4.   His pet turtle stayed by Ronnie and (him, he).

5.   Tomorrow, the principal and (they, them) will meet.

6.   Water from the puddle splashed Grandma and (us, we).

7.   Some of the girls and (him, he) are doing a skit.

8.   At the end of the day, several adults and (we, us) gathered to play baseball.

9.   Either Donna or (she, her) must have taken the letter to mail.

10.   May Justin and (me, I) put the chairs away?

11.   Please don't leave without Bo and (I, me).

12.   Uncle Stan saw Jeff and (she, her) at the hardware store.

Name_____

Date_____

Directions: Circle the correct pronoun.

Remember: Place your finger or fingers over the first part of the compound.   Then, reread the sentence and choose the correct pronoun.

1.   You may go with Jenny and (I, me).

2.   In the summer, his brother and (him, he) fished nearly every day.

3.   Would you like to go with Rocky and (we, us)?

4.   Miss Tarn and (them, they) walked to an art museum.

5.   Did you see Pastor Kern and (they, them) at the picnic?

6.   Allison and (us, we) make model airplanes.

7.   The artist painted a portrait of her grandmother and (she, her).

8.   A small child tapped Jerry and (him, he) on the legs with a tiny twig.

9.   You and (I, me) must bring cola to the party.

10.   During the camping trip, Amy and (she, her) waded in a stream.

11.   Did Mary and (he, him) leave for the fair?

12.   His jokes make Jalyn and (me, I) laugh.

13.   Ben, Ralph, and (me, I) played basketball after school.

14.   The card for his brother and (he, him) was from their aunt.

Possessive Pronouns

Possessive pronouns include:

my	**mine**
his	
her	**hers**
your	**yours**
its	
our	**ours**
their	**theirs**

<u>**My**, **his**, **her**, **your**, **its**, **our**, and **their** will come before a noun (or pronoun).</u>

Your *dog* is cute.

<u>**Mine**, **hers**, **yours**, **ours**, and **theirs** will occur after a noun.</u>

These *books* are **mine**.

A possessive pronoun does two things:

A.   A possessive pronoun takes the place of a noun.

B.   A possessive pronoun shows ownership.

Examples: a watch belonging to Kathy

Kathy's watch

her watch

toys belonging to the children

children's toys

their toys

🍓🍓🍓🍓🍓A possessive pronoun does **not** have an apostrophe (').🍓🍓🍓🍓🍓

Name_____

Date_____

A. Directions: Write a possessive pronoun on the line.

Example: A bird landed by me; _____its_____ head was blue.

1. The little boy is three years old; _____ hair is blonde.

2. Some children are playing tag; _____ mother is watching them.

3. I like to watch television; _____ favorite shows are basketball games.

4. My friends and I like to read; _____ town library is just down the street.

5. Patricia is flying to Utah; this is _____ first trip by airplane.

B. Directions: Write the possessive pronoun and the word it modifies (goes over to) on the line.

Example: Where is our photo album? _____our album_____

1. Their dad is a waiter.   _____

2. Your shoe is untied.   _____

3. Does her sister sew?   _____

4. We like our neighbors.   _____

5. My uncle lives near a lake.   _____

6. The cub went with its mother.   _____

7. Dee has a cut on her arm.   _____

Possessive Pronouns

Antecedents:

To have an antecedent, you must have a possessive pronoun.

Jill washed **her** car.

If you chose not to use a possessive pronoun, you would have to use the noun again:

Jill washed **Jill's** new car.

The possessive pronoun *her* refers back to Jill. **Jill is called the antecedent.**

Definition: An antecedent is the noun or pronoun to which the possessive pronoun refers.

> Example: The men talked about their new job.
>
> a. *Their* is a possessive pronoun.
> b. *Men* is the noun to which *their* refers back in the sentence.
>
> The *men* talked about the *men's* new job.
>
> c. *Men* is the antecedent of *their*.

Note: An antecedent will not be a word in a prepositional phrase.
The lamb with black ears followed its mother.
The lamb ~~with black ears~~ followed its mother.
antecedent for *its* = lamb

Antecedents agree in gender. If you use *her* in a sentence, the antecedent will be female.
> Incorrect: Joan wants a doll for *his* daughter.
> Correct: Joan wants a doll for *her* daughter.

Antecedents agree in number. If you use *her* in a sentence, the antecedent will be singular.
> Incorrect: Joan wants a doll for *their* daughter.
> Correct: Joan wants a doll for *her* daughter.

160

Name_____

Date_____

A. Directions: Write a possessive pronoun that agrees in number and gender with the boldfaced antecedent.

Example: **Julie** must take ____her____ film to be developed.

1. **Mark** asked to bring _____ dog along on the picnic.

2. The **girls** watched _____ brother swim a relay.

3. **You** must wait _____ turn.

4. My **family** and **I** are excited about _____ grandparents' visit.

B. Directions: Write the antecedent for the boldfaced possessive pronoun.

Example: _____Carl_____ Carl wants **his** change.

1. _____ A balloon has lost **its** string.

2. _____ Mrs. Parker sits on **her** porch every evening.

3. _____ Those robins built **their** nest early in the spring.

4. _____ A passenger picked up **her** purse and left the bus.

5. _____ Dad and I cleaned **our** entire house.

6. _____ You may bring **your** own towels to camp.

7. _____ Peter must drive **his** car to work.

8. _____ Paul, Barry, and Christy sailed on **their** boat.

Name_____

Date_____

Directions: Circle the correct word.

1.   The cat swished (its, it's) tail.

2.   (They're, Their) making cookies.

3.   Tell me if (its, it's) true.

4.   (They're, Their) brother is in college.

5.   (Its, It's) foot was caught in a trap.

6.   (You're, Your) cap is covered with dirt.

7.   I wonder if (they're, their) roof is leaking.

8.   Are you sure that (its, it's) raining?

9.   We hope (they're, their) feeling better.

10.   (You're, Your) dinner is ready.

11.   I know that (you're, your) upset.

12.   One of the pigeons hurt (its, it's) wing.

13.   I hope that (you're, your) chosen for the play.

14.   Was (they're, their) luggage lost?

Interrogative Pronouns

An Interrogative pronoun asks a question.

Interrogative pronouns include **who, whom, whose, which, and what**.

Examples: **Who** is coming with me?
For **whom** did you buy that?
Whose is that?
Which is right?
What did you do last night?

🍓🍓🍓🍓🍓🍓🍓🍓🍓🍓🍓🍓🍓🍓🍓🍓🍓🍓🍓🍓🍓🍓🍓🍓🍓🍓🍓🍓🍓🍓🍓🍓🍓🍓🍓🍓

LEARNING WHEN TO USE WHO AND WHOM:

1. *Who* is a nominative pronoun. *Who* will serve as subject of a sentence.

   Who is your teacher?   (subject)

2. *Whom* is an objective pronoun. *Whom* will serve as an object of a sentence.

   a. Object of a preposition:

      Incorrect: Who did you give that **to**?

Do not end a sentence with *to, for, with* or *at*!

      Correct: **To** whom did you give that?

Use <u>whom</u> after *to, for, with* or *at*!

      Correct: <u>For whom</u> is that gift?
      <u>From whom</u> is that note?
      <u>With whom</u> will you stay?
      <u>At whom</u> was the dodge ball thrown?

b. Direct object:

A direct object receives the action of a verb. Use *whom* as a direct object in a sentence that asks a question.

The ball hit **whom** on the foot?

🍓🍓🍓🍓🍓🍓🍓🍓🍓🍓🍓🍓🍓🍓🍓🍓🍓🍓🍓🍓🍓🍓🍓🍓🍓🍓🍓🍓🍓🍓🍓🍓🍓🍓🍓

What, **which**, and **whose** are pronouns when they stand alone. However, they serve as adjectives when they modify (go over to) a noun (or pronoun) in a sentence.

Examples:

What are you reading?	(pronoun)
What book are you reading? __**what book**__	(adjective)
Which do you like best?	(pronoun)
Which cake do you like best? __**which cake**__	(adjective)
Whose is this?	(pronoun)
Whose pencil is this? __**whose pencil**__	(adjective)

🍓When you see <u>what</u>, <u>which</u>, or <u>whose</u>, always check to see if it modifies or goes over to another word in the sentence.

Example: **Which *answer*** was correct?   (adjective)

If <u>what</u>, <u>which</u>, or <u>whose</u> stands alone, it serves as a pronoun.

Example: **Which** was chosen?   (pronoun)

We do not know to what the word ***which*** refers.

Name_____

Date_____

A. Directions: Write *who* or *whom* in the space provided.

Remember: **Who** is used as the subject of the sentence.
            Whom is used after prepositions (such as <u>to</u>, <u>for</u>, <u>with</u>, and <u>from</u>).

1. To _____ did you send that package?

2. _____ is your favorite singer?

3. You received a letter from _____?

4. After the game, _____ wants to walk home with me?

5. With _____ are you going to the zoo?

B. Directions: Write an appropriate interrogative pronoun.

Remember: Interrogative pronouns include **what**, **which**, **who**, **whose**, and **whom**.

1. _____ do you want to do?

2. For _____ did he ask?

3. _____ are these?

4. During the summer, _____ is his babysitter?

5. _____ pair of pants did Charlie buy?

6. _____ is your best friend?

Name_____   **PRONOUNS**
                                          Interrogative
Date_____

A. Directions: Write *who* or *whom* in the space provided.

Remember: *Who* is used as the subject of the sentence.
              Whom is used after prepositions (such as <u>to</u>, <u>for</u>, <u>with</u>, and <u>from</u>).

1. To _____ are you talking?

2. From _____ have you received a gift?

3. With _____ are you leaving?

4. Today, _____ would like to be first?

B. Directions: Write <u>P</u> if the boldfaced word serves as a pronoun.
              Write <u>A</u> if the boldfaced word serves as an adjective. Then, write the
              noun the boldfaced word modifies (goes over to).

    Example: __P__ **Which** do you want? _____

               __A__ **Which** cereal do you want? ____which cereal____

1. _____   **What** did he give you? _____

2. _____   **What** answer did he give you? _____

3. _____   **Which** do you want? _____

4. _____   **Which** piece of toast do you want? _____

5. _____   **Whose** is this? _____

6. _____   **Whose** car is in the driveway? _____

166

Name_____   **Pronoun Review**

Date_____

A. **Nominative Pronouns (used as subject of a sentence):**

Directions: Replace the boldfaced noun or nouns with a nominative pronoun.

1. My **dad** laughs often. _____ is very funny.

2. Jacob's **sister** is ten years old. _____ attends my church.

3. Our **family** loves winter. _____ like to ski.

4. For their vacation, **Misty** and **Sam** went to Kentucky. _____ went to Mammoth Cave.

5. _____ likes to _____.
        (your name)   **(something you like to do)**

    _____ like it because _____.

6. A **bird** flew onto a branch of a maple tree. _____ had a twig in its beak.

B. **Objective Pronouns:**

Directions: Replace the boldfaced noun with an objective pronoun.

1. Ask **Mary** to help you. Ask _____ to help you.

2. The mayor talked to the **people**. The mayor talked to _____.

3. Please take _____ with you. Please take _____ with you.   **(your name)**

4. A clown pointed at a huge yellow **balloon** and laughed. A clown pointed at _____ and laughed.

5. The aunt handed the baby **boy** to his mother. The aunt handed _____ to his mother.

C. **Nominative and Objective Pronouns:**

   Directions: Circle the correct pronoun.

1. A child helped (us, we) in the garden.

2. Yesterday, (I, Me) fixed my bicycle.

3. On Tuesdays, (he, him) helps at a hospital.

4. A nurse spoke with (them, they) about the patient.

5. That dog follows (he, him) everywhere.

6. (Us, We) might be going on a hike.

7. Mary grabbed her papers and scattered (they, them) on the table.

8. A small boy kicked (she, her) under the table.

9. Our mother scolded (us, we) for standing on a ladder.

D. **Compound Pronouns:**

   Directions: Circle the correct pronoun.

1. Please take Bonnie and (we, us) with you.

2. May Mike and (I, me) use your ball?

3. The cat just sat and stared at Jean and (him, he).

4. Autumn leaves fell on their teacher and (they, them).

5. Mr. King called my father and (I, me) yesterday.

E. **Possessive Pronouns**

Directions: Write the possessive pronoun and the word it modifies (goes over to) on the line.

1. Her hair is red. _____

2. Is your brother fifteen? _____

3. Some boys left their snacks on the floor. _____

4. Where is my red striped shirt? _____

5. Our relatives live in Maryland. _____

6. Mindy and Mort went with their friends to a zoo. _____

F. **Antecedents:**

Directions: Write the antecedent for the boldfaced pronoun on the line.

1. _____ Jamie showed **her** bandage to the class.

2. _____ The boy chose **his** own bedspread.

3. _____ Several dogs jump on **their** hind legs.

4. _____ A coyote hunted **its** food.

5. _____ One of their girls shows **her** pigs at the fair.

6. _____ Meg and she want **their** posters on the wall.

G. **Interrogative Pronouns:**

Directions: Circle the correct pronoun.

1. (Who, Whom) is the author of <u>Heidi</u>?

2. With (who, whom) did you go to the baseball game?

3. After your trip to Canada, to (who, whom) did you show your slides?

H. **Objective Pronouns:**

Directions: Write <u>P</u> if the boldfaced word serves as a pronoun.
    Write <u>A</u> if the boldfaced word serves as an adjective. Then, write
    the noun the boldfaced word modifies (goes over to).

Example: __A__ **What** reward was offered?   ____what reward_____

    __P__ **What** is your name? _____

1. _____   **Which** door was open? _____

2. _____   **What** did you decide? _____

3. _____   **Whose** key is on the floor? _____

4. _____   In **what** events did he enter? _____

5. _____   **Whose** is this? _____

6. _____   "**Which** do you prefer?" asked the clerk. _____

A. **Object of the Preposition:**

 Directions: Cross out any prepositional phrases. Label the object of the preposition - <u>O.P.</u>

1. A man waited on the street corner.

2. The sandwich for lunch is in this bag.

☃☃☃☃☃☃☃☃☃☃☃☃☃☃☃☃☃☃☃☃☃☃☃☃☃☃☃☃☃

B. **Prepositions:**

 Directions: Cross out any prepositional phrases. Underline the subject once and the verb/verb phrase twice. Label any direct object - <u>D.O.</u>

1. After dinner, Grandpa takes a short walk.

2. The librarian read a poem about a knight.

3. Gail brushes her teeth at bedtime.

☃☃☃☃☃☃☃☃☃☃☃☃☃☃☃☃☃☃☃☃☃☃☃☃☃☃☃☃☃

C. **Compound Subject:**
 Directions: Cross out any prepositional phrases. Underline the subject once and the verb/verb phrase twice.

 Remember: Compound means more than one.

1. His sister and brother belong to a basketball team.

2. Three letters and a magazine were thrown into the trash.

☃☃☃☃☃☃☃☃☃☃☃☃☃☃☃☃☃☃☃☃☃☃☃☃☃☃☃☃☃

D. **Imperative Sentences:**

 Directions: Cross out any prepositional phrases. Underline the subject once and the verb/verb phrase twice.

1. Please stand for the pledge.

2. Sit by the fire.

3. Print your name here.

E. **Compound Objects of the Preposition:**

Directions: Cross out any prepositional phrases. Underline the subject once
and the verb/verb phrase twice.

1. I went to Texas with my cousins and uncle.

2. Snow often falls in October or November.

🍓🍓🍓🍓🍓🍓🍓🍓🍓🍓🍓🍓🍓🍓🍓🍓🍓🍓🍓🍓🍓🍓🍓🍓🍓🍓🍓🍓🍓🍓🍓🍓🍓

F. **Compound Verbs:**

Directions: Cross out any prepositional phrases. Underline the subject once
and the verb/verb phrase twice.

1. A toddler lifted her toy and threw it.

2. George rides his bike and delivers newspapers.

🍓🍓🍓🍓🍓🍓🍓🍓🍓🍓🍓🍓🍓🍓🍓🍓🍓🍓🍓🍓🍓🍓🍓🍓🍓🍓🍓🍓🍓🍓🍓🍓🍓

G. **Infinitives:**

Directions: Cross out any prepositional phrases. Underline the subject once
and the verb twice. Place an infinitive in parenthesis (   ).

1. The gerbil likes to run in his cage.

2. Mr. Harper needs to go to the bank.

🍓🍓🍓🍓🍓🍓🍓🍓🍓🍓🍓🍓🍓🍓🍓🍓🍓🍓🍓🍓🍓🍓🍓🍓🍓🍓🍓🍓🍓🍓🍓🍓🍓

H. **Contractions:**

Directions: Write the contraction in the space provided.

1. we are - _____

5. you are - _____

2. who is - _____

6. I am - _____

3. are not - _____

7. cannot - _____

4. will not - _____

8. he is - _____

172

I. **Action Verb?:**

    Directions: Write <u>Yes</u> if the boldfaced verb shows action; write <u>No</u> if the boldfaced verb does not show action.

1. _____ His cat **drank** milk.   3. _____ The bell **sounds** loud.

2. _____ The child **grew** tired.   4. _____ A lady **planted** roses.

J. **Regular or Irregular:**

    Directions: Write <u>RV</u> if the verb is regular. Write <u>IV</u> if the verb is irregular.

Remember: Regular verbs add <u>ed</u> to the past and past participle.

1. _____ to count   3. _____ to teach   5. _____ to sit

2. _____ to fall   4. _____ to stir   6. _____ to rise

K. **Tenses:**

    Directions: Cross out any prepositional phrases. Underline the subject once and the verb/verb phrase twice. Write the tense on the line.
    Remember: The tenses that we have learned are *present*, *past*, and *future*.

1. _____ Donna writes letters daily.

2. _____ Donna wrote a letter to her aunt.

3. _____ Donna will write a letter to Bo tomorrow.

L. **Subject-Verb Agreement:**

    Directions: Circle the verb that agrees with the subject.

1. He (spend, spends) most of his time alone.

2. Each of the men (eat, eats) his lunch at noon.

3. Diane and Dirk (jog, jogs) three miles every day.   173

Name_____

Date_____

**Cumulative Review
Pronoun Unit**

M. Irregular Verbs:

Directions: Circle the correct verb.

1. Has Mr. Lind (came, come) yet?

2. Janice must have (flew, flown) to Denver early today.

3. Their coach should have (gave, given) the pitcher a new ball.

4. We have (lain, laid) two clean towels in the bathroom.

N. Concrete and Abstract Nouns:

Directions: Write C if the noun is concrete; write A if the noun is abstract.

1. _____ lemon   3. _____ honesty   5. _____ fog

2. _____ coin   4. _____ flag   6. _____ laughter

O. Common and Proper Nouns:

Directions: Write CN if the noun is common; write PN if the noun is proper.

1. _____ AMERICA   3. _____ FRIEND   5. _____ LAKE

2. _____ HORSE   4. _____ FRANCE   6. _____ DAVE

P. Noun Identification:

Directions: Underline any nouns in each sentence.

Remember: You may wish to circle determiners to help you find most nouns.

1. Two pies and a jello dessert were served at our picnic.

2. That bicycle with small wheels and an enormous seat is unusual.

3. Many deer stood in the meadow by their home.

174

Q. **Singular and Plural Nouns:**

Directions: Write the plural.

1. latch - _____

2. potato - _____

3. mouse - _____

4. tissue - _____

5. moose - _____

6. goose - _____

7. guess - _____

8. calf - _____

R. **Possessive Nouns:**

Directions: Write the possessive form.

1. a brush belonging to Nancy

_____

2. a hospital room shared by two patients

_____

3. friends of my uncle

_____

S. **Sentence Types:**

Directions: Write the sentence type in the space provided.
Remember: The four sentence types are declarative, interrogative, imperative, and exclamatory.

1. _____ Why did you do that?

2. _____ Peter asked his dad for the car.

3. _____ Give this to Ronnie.

4. _____ Yeah! We are allowed to go!

T. **Conjunctions and Interjections:**

Directions: Label any conjunction - CONJ.; label any interjection - INTJ.

1. A security guard and policeman spoke, but no decision was made.

2. Wow! Dad or Mom will drive us to an amusement park!

U. **Adjective?:**

Directions: Write <u>Yes</u> if the boldfaced word serves as an adjective. Write <u>No</u> if the boldfaced word does not serve as an adjective.

1. _____ His **flower** garden is blooming.

2. _____ A single **flower** was placed in a crystal vase.

3. _____ I liked **that** movie.

4. _____ I love **that**!

V. **Proper Adjectives:**

Directions: Capitalize any proper adjective.

1. An arizona sunset is colorful.

2. He drives his ford truck on the german roads.

W. **Degrees of Adjectives:**

Directions: Circle the correct answer.

1. This picture of you is (more pretty, prettier) than that one.

2. Sandra is the (shorter, shortest) triplet.

3. Of the two job offers, I think the first one is (better, best).

176

X. **Adjective Identification:**

Directions: Circle any adjectives.

Suggestion: First, look for limiting adjectives. Then, reread the sentence searching for descriptive adjectives.

1. His mother made three large banana splits with whipped cream.

2. That red tricycle with many colorful balloons is a birthday gift.

3. An oblong loaf of raisin bread was placed on our table.

Y. **Adverbs:**

Directions: Write the adverb form of the word.

1. crazy - _____   3. joyous - _____

2. sudden - _____   4. timid - _____

Z. **Adverbs - How?:**

Directions: Circle any adverbs that tell *how*.

1. He walks quickly in cold weather.

2. Several hikers walked noisily through the forest.

AA. **Adverbs - How?:**

Directions: Write the adverb form for the boldfaced word.

1. Stan is a **slow** driver. He drives _____.

2. The lady is a **soft** whistler. She whistles _____.

4. Mom and Dad are **hard** workers. They work _____.

BB. **Adverbs - Where?:**

Directions: Circle any adverbs that tell *where*.

1. You may go anywhere you like.

2. Our friends invited us over for dinner.

🍓🍓🍓🍓🍓🍓🍓🍓🍓🍓🍓🍓🍓🍓🍓🍓🍓🍓🍓🍓🍓🍓🍓🍓🍓🍓🍓🍓🍓🍓🍓🍓🍓🍓

CC. **Adverbs - To What Extent?:**

Directions: Circle any adverbs that tell *to what extent*.

1. Your project is very good.

2. This pancake syrup is not too sticky.

🍓🍓🍓🍓🍓🍓🍓🍓🍓🍓🍓🍓🍓🍓🍓🍓🍓🍓🍓🍓🍓🍓🍓🍓🍓🍓🍓🍓🍓🍓🍓🍓🍓🍓

DD. **Degrees of Adverbs:**
Directions: Circle the correct adverb form.

1. The artist drew this sketch (more carefully, most carefully) than that one.

2. Jamie's handwriting is (clearer, more clear) than his friend's.

3. Our new puppy is the (more energetic, most energetic) one of the four.

4. That jockey rode (harder, hardest) during his third race.

🍓🍓🍓🍓🍓🍓🍓🍓🍓🍓🍓🍓🍓🍓🍓🍓🍓🍓🍓🍓🍓🍓🍓🍓🍓🍓🍓🍓🍓🍓🍓🍓🍓🍓

EE. **Double Negatives:**
Directions: Circle the correct answer.

1. He wouldn't give (anyone, no one) a dollar.

2. They aren't inviting (no, any) children to their Christmas party.

3. He doesn't want (nothing, anything).

178

FRIENDLY LETTER

The **heading**, the **greeting**, the **body**, the **closing**, and the **signature** are the parts of a friendly letter. The greeting is also called the salutation.

A three-lined **formal** heading will be used. In **informal** letters, the date is frequently the only item included. However, the formal heading is important to know.

In a formal letter, as in all formal writing, abbreviations are not used. The **exception** to this is the postal code for states. A postal code is capitalized, and no punctuation is used.

Examples: New York = NY   Texas = TX
Arizona = AZ   Virginia = VA

🍓🍓🍓🍓🍓🍓🍓🍓🍓🍓🍓🍓🍓🍓🍓🍓🍓🍓🍓🍓🍓🍓🍓🍓🍓🍓🍓🍓🍓🍓🍓🍓🍓🍓🍓🍓🍓🍓

FRIENDLY LETTER PARTS:

POST OFFICE BOX
or
HOUSE NUMBER AND STREET NAME

heading   CITY, STATE   ZIP CODE

COMPLETE DATE (not abbreviated)

greeting Dear (Person)   ,

    The body is also called the message. It is written here. You indent at least five letters. You may skip a line between the greeting and the body.

body Note that you have margins on each side of the paper.

    Remember that every time you change topics, you begin a new paragraph.

closing   Your friend,
signature   Writer's Name

Commas:

1. Be sure to put a **comma** between the city and state in the second line of the heading.

2. Be sure to put a **comma** after the name in the greeting.

3. Be sure to put a **comma after the closing.** However, **no comma** is placed between the state and the zip code.

Capitalization:

1. Capitalize the first word and a name in a greeting. If you can insert a person's name, capitalize it.

   Examples:

   > **Dear B**etty,
   > **Dear S**on,   (Son is capitalized because you can insert the son's name.)
   >
   > **M**y dear friend,

2. Capitalize only the first word of a closing.

   Examples:

   > **T**ruly yours,
   > **Y**our friend,

3. The first word of each line of the heading begins at the same place. The same is true of the closing and signature. Also, the heading, closing, and signature are lined up. **You should be able to place a ruler in front of the heading, the closing, and the signature and draw a straight line.**

4. A letter should not be crowded at the top of a page. The number of lines skipped between the heading and body will depend on the length of the message. The letter should be spaced down the page.

Envelope:

1. Place a return address in the upper left hand corner. The purpose of the return address is so that the post office can return the letter to you if, for some reason, the letter cannot be delivered.

Look at the sample return address on the envelope below.
  - On the first line, write your name.

  - On the second line, write your house number and street name. Be sure to capitalize your entire street name. In formal letters, do not use abbreviations.

  - On the third line, write your city, state, and zip code. Be sure that you place a comma between the city and state. Do not place a comma between state and zip code. You may use a postal code for the state.

  - **Do not include the date.** The post office doesn't need this information.

2. The main address is important. It contains the name and address of the person who will be receiving your letter.

    Look at the sample main address on the envelope below.

    - On the first line, write the name of the person to whom you are sending the letter.

    - On the second line, write that person's house number and street name. Be sure to capitalize the entire street name. Do not use abbreviations.

    - On the third line, write the city, state, and zip code of the person who will be receiving your letter. Be sure that you place a comma between the city and state. Do not place a comma between state and zip code. You may use a postal code for the state.

Your First and Last Name
House Number and Street Name   **return address**
City, State   Zip Code

                    main address   Person to Whom You Are Sending the Letter
                                              Person's House Number and Street Name
                                              City, State   Zip Code

---

Rule 1: Capitalize a person's name.

      Examples: **T**ama

                   Yuri **T**odman

Rule 2: Capitalize initials.

      Examples: **K**oko **A. K**irk

                   L. B. Shane

Rule 3: Capitalize a title with a name.

      Examples: **A**unt **K**esi   **M**rs. **A**nne **W**ing

                   Governor **C**ontos   **D**r. **L**iston

     However, do not capitalize a title if it is a career choice.

       Abel wants to become a doctor.

       Mrs. Keokuk is running for governor of her state.

Rule 4: Capitalize the pronoun I.

Rule 5: Capitalize the first word of a sentence.

🍓🍓

Directions: Write your answer on the line.

1.   Write the first and last name of your best friend. _____

2.   Write your name. Include your middle initial. _____

3.   Write the name of a relative such as your aunt, uncle, grandmother, or grandfather

     with a name.   Example: Aunt Hetty   _____

4.   Write a complete sentence using the pronoun I. _____

     _____

5.   If you would become a senator, what would your name be with the title added?

     Write it. _____

6.   Write your teacher's name. Use Miss, Mrs., or Mr. with it. _____

182

Name_____

Date_____

Rule 1: Capitalize a person's name.

Examples: **T**ama
Yuri **T**odman

Rule 2: Capitalize initials.

Examples: **K**oko **A. K**irk
L. B. Shane

Rule 3: Capitalize a title with a name.

Examples: **A**unt **K**esi   **M**rs. **A**nne **W**ing
Governor **C**ontos   **D**r. **L**iston

However, do not capitalize a title if it is a career choice.

Abel wants to become a doctor.
Mrs. Keokuk is running for governor of her state.

Rule 4: Capitalize the pronoun I.

Rule 5: Capitalize the first word of a sentence.

Directions: Write the capital letter above any word that needs to be capitalized.

1. mrs. isi p. bloom is their neighbor.

2. may aren and i have milk?

3. yesterday, governor yassie visited us.

4. he is mayor roy h. rigas.

5. mr. and mrs. s. t. hull won a trip.

6. tara and miss brock met with dr. harden.

7. ralph, thomas, and mosi went to church together.

8. barton e. preston is their state's new governor.

Name_____

Date_____

Rule 6: Capitalize the name of a school, college, hospital, or library.

Examples: Liberty School   Boswell Hospital

Shippensburg University   Mesquite Library

Do not capitalize a school, college, hospital, or library unless a specific name is given.

We like to go to the library.
He attends a junior high school.

Rule 7: Capitalize the name of a business.

Examples: London Company   Market Cable, Inc.

Kodiac Express   My Favorite Florist

Clover Jewelers   Computers Plus

Lighthouse Bakery   Parrot Food Club

Magic Fashions   Princess Travel

Triumph Hotel   Aster Medical Equipment

Ribbons Drugstore   Palm Department Store

Bell Shopping Center   Westwood Mall

Directions: Write your answer on the line.

1. _____ is near my house.
                    (name of school)

2. I sometimes eat at _____.
                              (name of restaurant)

3. A hospital near my home is _____.

4. My _____ works at _____.
        (person)   (name of business)

5. I buy _____ at _____.
              (item)   (name of business)

184

Rule 6: Capitalize the name of a school, college, hospital, or library.

Examples: Liberty School   Boswell Hospital

Shippensburg University   Mesquite Library

Do not capitalize a school, college, hospital, or library unless a specific name is given.

We like to go to the library.
He attends a junior high school.

Rule 7: Capitalize the name of a business.

Examples:	
London **C**ompany	**M**arket **C**able, Inc.
Kodiac **E**xpress	**M**y **F**avorite **F**lorist
Clover **J**ewelers	**C**omputers **P**lus
Lighthouse **B**akery	**P**arrot **F**ood **C**lub
Magic **F**ashions	**P**rincess **T**ravel
Triumph **H**otel	**A**ster **M**edical **E**quipment
Ribbons **D**rugstore	**P**alm **D**epartment **S**tore
Bell **S**hopping **C**enter	**W**estwood **M**all

Directions: Write the capital letter above any word that needs to be capitalized.

1. seth attends latham college.

2. she lives near a middle school by dover library.

3. his brother works at garret tile company.

4. they ate lunch at royce's texas cafe.

5. grandmother entered york hospital for tests.

6. sparkle cleaning service just opened for business.

7. their neighbor owns cameo bakery near baltimore art school.

Rule 8: Capitalize days and months.

      Examples: Tuesday   January

Rule 9: Capitalize holidays and special days.

      Examples: Thanksgiving   Independence Day

Rule 10: Capitalize the name of special events.

Examples:		
Tampa Arts Festival	**Arizona Senior Olympics**	
Kingsdale Carnival	**Phoenix Open Golf Tournament**	
Four Seasons Rodeo	**Orange Bowl Parade.**	
All State Horse Show	**Barrett Jackson Auto Auction**	

Do not capitalize the event unless a specific name is given.

Jan played in a golf tournament.

Directions: Write your answer on the line.

1. My favorite day of the week is _____.

2. Do you like Thanksgiving or Christmas better? _____

3. My favorite holiday is _____.

4. My favorite special day is _____.

5. My birthday is in the month of _____.

6. Another month that I like is _____ because _____

_____

7. A special event I attended this year was _____.

8. A special event I would like to attend is _____.

Rule 8: Capitalize days and months.

      Examples: Tuesday   January

Rule 9: Capitalize holidays and special days.

      Examples: Thanksgiving   Independence Day

Rule 10: Capitalize the name of special events.

      Examples: Tampa Arts Festival   Arizona Senior Olympics

                         Bonneauville Carnival   Phoenix Open Golf Tournament

                         Four Seasons Rodeo   Orange Bowl Parade.

                         All State Horse Show   Barrett Jackson Auto Auction

Do not capitalize the event unless a specific name is given.

Jan played in a golf tournament.

Directions: Write the capital letter above any word that needs to be capitalized.

1. on arbor day, their class planted trees.

2. we will go to the south mountain fair on monday.

3. pennsylvania sampler crafts show was held last year.

4. on saturday, october 18, we attended an art show.

5. the rose bowl parade will be held again this year.

6. last valentine's day, their parents went to the lincoln sweethearts' ball.

7. the girls met in march to celebrate st. patrick's day.

8. is the fiesta bowl parade held on new year's day?

9. each july, our family enjoys watching cowboys compete at the prescott rodeo.

Name_____

Date_____

Rule 11: Capitalize the name of a language.

      Examples: **E**nglish   **G**erman

Rule 12: Capitalize the first word in a line of poetry.

      Examples: **T**hough I travel to the song of a fife,
                            And you to the sound of the distant drum,
                            We sing the music of friendship.

Rule 13: Capitalize the first word of a greeting and a closing of a letter.

      Examples: **D**ear Tara,   **T**ruly yours,

Rule 14: Capitalize brand names but not the products.

      Examples: **A**ppleland juice   **L**ittle **A**ngel baby shoes

Directions: Write your answer on the line.

1.   The language I speak is _____.

2.   I would also like to speak _____.

3.   If I were to write a letter, the greeting would say: _____.

4.   The closing of my letter would say: _____.

5.   My favorite cereal is _____   _____.
                              (brand name)   (product)

6.   I have bought _____ at a _____ store.
                        (brand name + product)   (type)

7.   Write a line of poetry that rhymes with the one given:

    Through the woods came a big brown bear,

    _____

Rule 11: Capitalize the name of a language.

        Examples: **E**nglish   **G**erman

Rule 12: Capitalize the first word in a line of poetry.

        Examples: **T**hough I travel to the song of a fife,
                    And you to the sound of the distant drum,
                    We sing the music of friendship.

Rule 13: Capitalize the first word of a greeting and a closing of a letter.

        Examples: **D**ear Tara,   **T**ruly yours,

Rule 14: Capitalize brand names but not the products.

        Examples: **A**ppleland juice   **L**ittle Angel baby shoes

Directions: Write the capital letter above any word that needs to be capitalized.

1. is spanish spoken here?

2. GREETING: dear nikko,

3. his dad teaches german at a high school.

4. CLOSING: your friend,

5. lisa likes harbor iced tea.

6. poetry: in the days of olden year,
               lived Mary Anna Doone,
               so sweet, so pretty, and so fair,
               that all the men did swoon.

7. my dear cousin,
       I'll be visiting you in August.   Let's roast peppy time hot dogs over a fire!
                            love,
                            Toya

Rule 15: Capitalize Mother, Dad, and other words if you can insert a person's name.

Example: **D**id **M**om buy cookies?

(If *Jamilla* is the mom's name, you can insert it. Did *Jamilla* buy cookies? You can replace *Mom* with *Jamilla*; therefore, *Mom* is capitalized.

Do not capitalize Mother, Dad, and other words if <u>my</u>, <u>his</u>, <u>her</u>, <u>your</u>, <u>its</u>, <u>our</u>, or <u>their</u> comes before it.

Example: My mom is very funny.

Rule 16: Capitalize historical events.

Example: **A**merican **R**evolution

Battle of **G**ettysburg

Rule 17: Capitalize the first word of a direct quotation.

Example: Alona said, "**T**hanks for the gift."

Do not capitalize the word following a quotation unless it is a proper noun.

Example: "**Y**ou're welcome," said Tansy.

Directions: Write the capital letter above any word that needs to be capitalized.

1. he asked, "are you coming along?"

2. "yes," replied his friend.

3. did grandma buy chocolate chip cookies?

4. his father watched a show about the battle of concord.

5. does aunt trina like to read about the civil war?

6. the police officer said, "we will help you."

Rule 15: Capitalize Mother, Dad, and other words if you can insert a person's name.

> Example: **D**id **M**om buy cookies?

> (If *Jamilla* is the mom's name, you can insert it. Did *Jamilla* buy cookies? You can replace *Mom* with *Jamilla*; therefore, *Mom* is capitalized.

> **Do not capitalize Mother, Dad, and other words if <u>my</u>, <u>his</u>, <u>her</u>, <u>your</u>, <u>its</u>, <u>our</u>, or <u>their</u> comes before it.**

> > Example: My mom is very funny.

Rule 16: Capitalize historical events.

> > Example: **A**merican **R**evolution

> > **B**attle of **G**ettysburg

Rule 17: Capitalize the first word of a direct quotation.

> > Example: Alona said, "**T**hanks for the gift."

> **Do not capitalize the word following a quotation unless it is a proper noun.**

> > Example: "**Y**ou're welcome," said Tansy.

Directions: Write the capital letter above any word that needs to be capitalized.

1. he enjoys briar patch fruit cocktail.

2. "will you open the door for me?" asked his mother.

3. yesterday, dad mowed the lawn.

4. does uncle lazlo like lady friday's apple sauce?

5. we studied about the french and indian war.

6. "let's eat soon," said the boy.   191

Name_____

Date_____

Rule 18: Capitalize the first word, the last word, and all important words of any title. Do not capitalize *a, an, the, and, but, or, nor,* **or** <u>**prepositions of four or less letters**</u> **unless they are the first or last word of a title. Capitalize all other words.**

Examples: "Jack and Jill"

<u>The Indian in the Cupboard</u>

Capitalize any verb in a title.

"W<u>h</u>at <u>I</u>s Music?"

Rule 19: Capitalize the Roman numerals and the letters of the first major topics in an outline. Capitalize the first word in an outline.

Examples: I. **S**ummer activities

A. Swimming

B. Arts and crafts

II. **W**inter activities

Directions: Write the capital letter above any word that needs to be capitalized.

1. CAPITALIZE THESE TITLES:

a. "internet"
b. <u>the fire cat</u>
c. <u>sheep in a shed</u>
d. <u>the legs of the moon</u>
e. <u>the sky is falling</u>

2. i. types of flowers

a. flowers with bulbs
b. flowers with roots

ii. types of ferns

192

Rule 18: Capitalize the first word, the last word, and all important words of any title. Do not capitalize *a*, *an*, *the*, *and*, *but*, *or*, *nor,* **or prepositions of four or less letters unless they are the first or last word of a title. Capitalize all other words.**

> Examples: "Jack and Jill"
>
> The Indian in the Cupboard

Capitalize any verb in a title.

> "What Is Music?"

Rule 19: Capitalize the Roman numerals and the letters of the first major topics in an outline. Capitalize the first word in an outline.

> Examples: I.   Summer activities
>
> **A.** Swimming
>
> **B.** Arts and crafts
>
> II.   Winter activities

🍓🍓🍓🍓🍓🍓🍓🍓🍓🍓🍓🍓🍓🍓🍓🍓🍓🍓🍓🍓🍓🍓🍓🍓🍓🍓🍓🍓🍓🍓🍓🍓🍓🍓

Directions: Write the capital letter above any word that needs to be capitalized.

1. i.   reference books

> a.   atlases
>
> b.   dictionaries and gazetteers

 ii.   fiction books

2. CAPITALIZE THESE TITLES:

> a.   children in history
>
> b.   "spring thaw"
>
> c.   the cabin faced west
>
> d.   rosie's fishing trip
>
> e.   the girl who could fly

Name_____

Date_____

Rule 20: Capitalize the name of buildings, canals, tunnels, roads, and bridges.

Examples: Lincoln Memorial   Turner Turnpike

Erie Canal   Interstate 270

Blueridge Tunnel   London Bridge

Rule 21: Capitalize the name of a geographic place:

continent	-	North America	ocean	-	Pacific Ocean
country	-	United States	sea	-	Bering Sea
state	-	Nebraska	gulf	-	Gulf of Mexico*
county	-	Franklin County	lake	-	Lake Superior
township	-	Mt. Joy Township	river	-	Missouri River
town or city	-	Dublin	streams	-	Miller Creek
regions	-	East	cave	-	Cove Cave
island	-	Hawaii	canyon	-	Bryce Canyon
mountain(s)	-	Mt. Rushmore	spring	-	Hot Springs
		Rocky Mountains	valley	-	Death Valley
forest	-	Tonto National Forest	dam	-	Hoover Dam
park	-	Sunset Park	desert	-	Gobi Desert

Directions: Write the capital letter above any word that needs to be capitalized.

1. santa claus is the name of a town in indiana.

2. is richardson highway in alaska?

3. hartwell dam is on the savannah river.

4. garden wall mountain is in glacier national park.

5. the fiji islands are in the pacific ocean.

6. have you been on the arlington memorial bridge?

7. otter tail county in minnesota has over a thousand lakes.

Rule 20: Capitalize the name of buildings, canals, tunnels, roads, and bridges.

	Examples:	Lincoln Memorial	Turner Turnpike
		Erie Canal	Interstate 270
		Blueridge Tunnel	London Bridge

Rule 21: Capitalize the name of a geographic place:

continent	-	North America	ocean	-	Pacific Ocean
country	-	United States	sea	-	Bering Sea
state	-	Nebraska	gulf	-	Gulf of Mexico
county	-	Franklin County	lake	-	Lake Superior
township	-	Mt. Joy Township	river	-	Missouri River
town or city	-	Dublin	streams	-	Miller Creek
regions	-	East	cave	-	Cove Cave
island	-	Hawaii	canyon	-	Bryce Canyon
mountain(s)	-	Mt. Rushmore	spring	-	Hot Springs
		Rocky Mountains	valley	-	Death Valley
forest	-	Tonto National Forest	dam	-	Hoover Dam
park	-	Sunset Park	desert	-	Gobi Desert

Directions: Write the capital letter above any word that needs to be capitalized.

1. the colorado desert is in southern california.

2. they always go to lake powell to fish.

3. is australia the smallest continent?

4. the cascade mountains are in oregon.

5. have you ever been in the lincoln tunnel?

6. we went to gallagher canyon in cozad, nebraska.

7. jewel cave is in the black hills of south dakota.

Rule 22: Capitalize the name of an organization.

> Examples: **4-H Club**   International Platform Association

> **Do not capitalize prepositions of four or less letters in names.**
> Girl Scouts of America

Rule 23: Capitalize the name of a religion, religious documents, and for a supreme being.

> Examples: **God**
>
> **Torah**
>
> **Allah**

Rule 24: Capitalize the name of a church, synagogue, temple, or other religious dwellings.

Directions: Write the capital letter above any word that needs to be capitalized.

1. is micah's temple located in that village?

2. jina and bianca read a book about the christian faith.

3. patterson lion's club meets in a local church.

4. the boy scouts of america held a jamboree.

5. a jewish rabbi read from the tanak.

6. the diamond riding club has just formed.

7. st. francis xavier church is beautiful.

Date_____

Rule 22: Capitalize the name of an organization.

  Examples: **4-H C**lub   **I**nternational **P**latform **A**ssociation

  Do not capitalize prepositions of four or less letters in names.
  Girl **S**couts <u>of</u> **A**merica

Rule 23: Capitalize the name of a religion, religious documents, and for a supreme being.

  Examples: **G**od
          Torah
          Allah

Rule 24: Capitalize the name of a church, synagogue, temple, or other religious dwellings.

🍓🍓🍓🍓🍓🍓🍓🍓🍓🍓🍓🍓🍓🍓🍓🍓🍓🍓🍓🍓🍓🍓🍓🍓🍓🍓🍓🍓🍓🍓🍓🍓

Directions: Write the capital letter above any word that needs to be capitalized.

1. our meeting is held at chapel hill church.

2. mothers against drunk drivers is an active organization.

3. deka is doing a report about the hindu religion.

4. an organization called valley big brothers is popular.

5. ivan's brother attends temple beth emeth.

6. my cousin belongs to the york kiwanis club.

7. the first five books of the old testament are called the pentateuch.

Name_____   **DO NOT CAPITALIZE**

Date_____

Rule 1: **Do not capitalize north, south, east, or west when they are used as directions.**

Example: I live north of the post office.

Capitalize the direction when it appears with a geographic place.

Sandy lives at 224 East Elm Street.

Rule 2: **Do not capitalize school subjects unless they state a language, or they are numbered.**

Examples: I like English.
Is Art I offered?
My favorite subjects are science and math.

Rule 3: **Do not capitalize seasons of the year.**

Examples: spring   winter

Rule 4: **Do not capitalize foods, games, musical instruments, animals, diseases, and plants.**

foods:	apple	hamburger
*games:**	checkers	basketball
musical instruments:	guitar	piano
diseases:	chicken pox	flu
plant:	daisy	pine tree
animals:	dog	ape

*Capitalize trademarked games such as Monopoly.

Directions: Write your answer on the line.

1.   My favorite season of the year is _____.

2.   My favorite subject is _____.

3.   I live _____ (direction) of the closest store.

4.   I like to play _____.

5.   The animal I like best is the _____.

6.   My favorite food is _____.

7.   The musical instrument I play (or might like to play) is the _____.

198

Name_____

Date_____

Rule 1: **Do not capitalize north, south, east, or west when they are used as directions.**

> Example: I live north of the post office.
>
> **Capitalize the direction when it appears with a geographic place.**
>
> Sandy lives at 224 East Elm Street.

Rule 2: **Do not capitalize school subjects unless they state a language, or they are numbered.**

> Examples: I like English.
> Is Art I offered?
> My favorite subjects are science and math.

Rule 3: **Do not capitalize seasons of the year.**

> Examples: spring   winter

Rule 4: **Do not capitalize foods, games, musical instruments, animals, diseases, and plants.**

foods:	apple	hamburger
*games:**	checkers	basketball
musical instruments:	guitar	piano
diseases:	chicken pox	flu
plant:	daisy	pine tree
animals:	dog	ape

Capitalize trademarked games such as Monopoly.

Directions: Write a capital letter above any word that needs to be capitalized.

1. has your father ever had the chicken pox?

2. teresa planted pansies on the west side of her house.

3. during the winter, many deer roam those woods.

4. her sister started playing the flute last year.

5. their football team met at the field located at 150 south Main Street.

6. jordan likes science, spelling, english, and history.

Name_____

Date_____

Directions: Write the capital letter above any word that needs to be capitalized.

1. the waiter asked, "may i help you?"

2. lynn attends harvard university.

3. have you seen mother's wallet?

4. a methodist church is on park street.

5. kyle served gorton's fish with apple fritters.

6. is colonial motel near williamsburg, virginia?

7. last wednesday, mayor tornbee went sailing.

8. his dad works at pretzel plus shop.

9. is banks island in the beaufort sea?

10. the poet, ralph waldo emerson, wrote the following lines about success:

   to appreciate beauty;

   to find the best in others;

11. the american red cross began during the civil war.

12. does dr. brine work at st. joseph's hospital?

13. hannah r. roger's new address in chicago is 510 south ash lane.

14. he plays the saxophone on a riverboat on the mississippi river.

15. does senator stone belong to the payson women's club?

Name_____   **CAPITALIZATION**
                                         Review

Date_____

Directions: Write the capital letter above any word that needs to be capitalized.

1. their grandmother owns apple tree fashions.

2. dear sammy,

        let's go to michaux state forest next saturday.

                your cousin,

                brad

3. a patient with the flu entered dr. fox's office.

4. cheyenne frontier days are held in the state of wyoming.

5. we crossed a bridge near the thomas jefferson memorial.

6. did they go to the gulf of california last spring?

7. the country of greece joined the north atlantic treaty organization in 1952.

8. Capitalize these titles:

    a. <u>simply fun</u>

    b. <u>wingman on ice</u>

    c. <u>a pair of red clogs</u>

    d. "here's a happy song"

9. the battle of clearwater took place in idaho.

10. a poem begins, "my candle burns at both ends."

11. has mother ever been to barren island off canada?

Directions: Write the capital letter above any word that needs to be capitalized.

1.   their family attends united christian church.

2.   the guide said, "welcome to our museum."

3.   egg harbor is a village on green bay.

4.   the draft horse and mule festival is held in virginia.

5.   their sister read the last leaf by o. henry.

6.   my friend and i went to varsity barber shop today.

7.   kent likes history at mesa high school.

8.   dear mr. price,

        we will meet with you in dallas next summer.

                                    sincerely yours,
                                    captain briggs

9.   we took interstate 495 last november.

10.   several girls played chess at a school on locust avenue.

11.   a librarian read peggy's new brother at denton library.

12.   we celebrate columbus day on october 12.

13.   i.   famous people in history

        a.   women

        b.   men

      ii.   famous animals in history

PUNCTUATION

PERIOD (.):

Rule 1: **Place a period at the end of a declarative sentence.**

I purchased a box of tissues.

Rule 2: **Place a period at the end of an imperative sentence.**

Press this button.

Rule 3: **Place a period after initials.**

Charity K. Pope

Rule 4: **Place a period after an abbreviation for days.**

Sunday - Sun.	Thursday - Thurs., Thur.*
Monday - Mon.	Friday - Fri.
Tuesday - Tues., Tue.*	Saturday - Sat.
Wednesday - Wed.	

*The first abbreviation is preferred.

Rule 5: **Place a period after the abbreviation for months.**

January - Jan.	September - Sept.
February - Feb.	October - Oct.
March - Mar.	November - Nov.
April - Apr.	December - Dec.
August - Aug.	

Note: May, June, and July have no abbreviations.

Rule 6: **Place a period after the abbreviation of titles.**

Mr. - Mister
Mrs. - title used before a married woman's name
Ms. - title that does not show if a woman is married or unmarried
Dr. - Doctor
Sen. - Senator
Gen. - General
Pres. - President

Do not place a period after Miss used as a title: Miss Barnett

Rule 7:   **Place a period after the name of places.**

St. - Street   Holly St.
Ave. - Avenue   Victory Ave.
Ln. - Lane   Marker Ln.
Dr. - Drive   Jefferson Dr.
Mt. - Mountain   Mt. Everest
Mts. - Mountains   Rocky Mts.
U.S. - United States
S. Am. - South America

Always use a dictionary to check for correct abbreviations.

Use the two letter **postal code** without a period for an abbreviation of states.

MO - Missouri   OH - Ohio
NM - New Mexico   WA - Washington

A postal code list can be found in the back of many dictionaries.

Rule 8:   **Place a period after many abbreviations.**

Co. - Company
A. D. - in the year of our Lord
P. M. or p. m. - from noon until midnight

Always use a dictionary to check for correct abbreviations.

If a sentence ends with an abbreviation, do not place an additional period.

Henry VIII of England was born in 1491 A.D.

Do not place a period after metric units: m = meter

Rule 9:   **Place a period after the letter(s) and number(s) in an outline.**

I.   Foods
  A.   Vegetables
  B.   Fruits
    1.   Cherries
    2.   Oranges
204   II. Drinks

Name_____

Date_____

Directions: Place a period where needed.

1. Write the correct abbreviation for each day of the week.

    a.   Monday - _____   e.   Thursday - _____

    b.   Wednesday - _____   f.   Saturday - _____

    c.   Friday - _____   g.   Sunday - _____

    d.   Tuesday - _____

2. Write the correct abbreviation for each month of the year.

    a.   September - _____   f.   November - _____

    b.   October - _____   g.   December - _____

    c.   March - _____   h.   January - _____

    d.   April - _____   i.   February - _____

    e.   August - _____

3. Write the correct abbreviation for the following:

    a.   Maple Street - _____

    b.   Doctor Prance - _____

    c.   North America - _____

    d.   Captain Troy - _____

    e.   Governor Hamel - _____

    f.   South Dakota - _____

    g.   Ural Mountains - _____

Name_____

Date_____

A. Directions: Place a period where needed.

1. Dr Cathy P Banks is our friend

2. Her address is 20 N Stratton St

3. Give this to Mrs Pyne, please

4. She was born Wed , Dec 27

5. I Types of cats

    A Siamese

    B Persian

  II Types of dogs

6. They went to Eur in Sept

7. Is Mt Baldy in Arizona?

B. Directions: Write the abbreviation.

    1. Tuesday - _____

    2. Thursday - _____

    3. November - _____

    4. January - _____

    5. February - _____

    6. Company - _____

    7. Wednesday - _____

Name_____

Date_____

Rule 1: **Use an apostrophe in a contraction to show where a letter or letters have been omitted.**

wasn't = was not   she's = she is

Rule 2: **Use an apostrophe to show possession (ownership):**
   A. **If the word is singular (one), add apostrophe + <u>s</u>.**

a man's watch   one girl's tent

Even if the singular noun ends in <u>s</u>, add '<u>s</u>.
Dennis's sister

   B. **If the word is plural (more than one) and ends in <u>s</u>, add an apostrophe after the <u>s</u>.**

dogs' owner   girls' coach

   C. **If the word is plural (more than one) and does not end in <u>s</u>, add apostrophe + <u>s</u>.**

singular:	child	woman
plural:	children	women
plural possessive:	children's camp	women's team

🍓🍓🍓🍓🍓🍓🍓🍓🍓🍓🍓🍓🍓🍓🍓🍓🍓🍓🍓🍓🍓🍓🍓🍓🍓🍓🍓🍓🍓🍓🍓🍓

Directions: Write the possessive.

1. a car belonging to Ernie: _____

2. a dish belonging to three cats: _____

3. fields belonging to a farmer: _____

4. the sleeve of a shirt: _____

5. the father of several boys: _____

6. dogs owned by Chris: _____

7. magazines belonging to her sister: _____

Rule 1: Use an apostrophe in a contraction to show where a letter or letters have been omitted.

wasn't = was not   she's = she is

Rule 2: Use an apostrophe to show possession (ownership):

A. If the word is singular (one), add apostrophe + s.

a man's watch   one girl's tent

Even if the singular noun ends in s, add 's.

Dennis's sister

B. If the word is plural (more than one) and ends in s, add an apostrophe after the s.

dogs' owner   girls' coach

C. If the word is plural (more than one) and does not end in s, add apostrophe + s.

singular:	child	woman
plural:	children	women
plural possessive:	children's camp	women's team

A. Directions: Write the possessive.

1. buttons on a remote: _____

2. a restroom belonging to all men: _____

3. a trail for runners: _____

B. Directions: Insert needed apostrophes.

1. "Dont forget your umbrella," said Bennys mother.

2. Her brothers best friend cant go with us.

3. Wheres Cynthias new coat?

4. Marys sister likes to swing at a childrens playground.

Rule 1: **Use a comma to invert a name. Place the last name, a comma, and the first name.**

Lincoln, Abe

⬆

If the middle name or initial is given, place the middle name or initial after the first name.

Swanson, Susan Lee   or   Swanson, Susan L.

Rule 2: **Place a comma after the greeting of a friendly letter.**

Dear Christine,

⬆

Rule 3: **Place a comma after the closing of any letter.**

Love,

Jo ⬆

Rule 4: **Place a comma after three or more items in a series.**
Do not place a comma after the last item in a series.

He handed a dime, two nickels, and a quarter to me.

⬆   ⬆

🍓🍓🍓🍓🍓🍓🍓🍓🍓🍓🍓🍓🍓🍓🍓🍓🍓🍓🍓🍓🍓🍓🍓🍓🍓🍓🍓🍓🍓🍓🍓🍓🍓

A. Directions: Write answers on the line.

1. Write your last name and then your first name. _____

2. Write a friend's last name and then the first name. _____

B. Directions: Insert needed commas.

1. Wendy Brian and I had fun at the beach.

2. Dear Mike

I'll see you soon!

Your friend
Corrine

3. We ate chicken potatoes and pasta at the picnic.

Rule 5: **Use a comma to separate introductory words.**
Frequently used introductory words are *yes*, *no*, and *well*.

Yes, you are right.

⬆

Rule 6: **Use a comma with a noun of direct address.**

A. If the person is addressed (spoken to) at the beginning of a sentence, place a comma **after** the person's name.

Ron, do you want a banana?

⬆

B. If the person is addressed (spoken to) at the end of a sentence, place a comma **before** the person's name.

Do you want a banana, Ron?

⬆

C. If the person is addressed (spoken to) in the middle of a sentence, place a comma **before** and **after** the person's name.

Do you, Ron, want a banana?

⬆ ⬆

Directions: Insert a comma where needed.

1. Mrs. Ross have you voted?

2. No I don't want any more pizza.

3. Would you like a brownie Jenny?

4. Yes an ambulance has been called.

5. I know Gloria that you're usually on time.

6. Well I'm finally finished.

7. Yes Patty you may begin.

Rule 7:   Use a comma to make a sentence clear.

During the day, games were played.

⬆

Rule 8:   Use a comma to set off interrupters.
Words and phrases often used as interrupters are: *by the way*, *therefore*, *however*, *in fact*, and *I believe*. Of course, there are others.

This covered bridge, in fact, was built in 1875.

⬆   ⬆

Rule 9:   Use a comma at the end of most direct quotations.
A direct quotation states exactly what the person says.

"I'll help you," said Lenny.

⬆

If the person who is making the statement is given first, place a comma after the person's name.

Sally said, "My lunch box is missing."

⬆

Directions: Insert a comma where needed.

1. Your dad I believe just left for work.

2. "I'll trade you baseball cards " said Anthony.

3. This ring in fact was my grandmother's wedding band.

4. Holly said   "I'm going to the library."

5. That water however may not be safe to drink.

6. By the way has anyone asked you to go tubing?

7. Loni whispered   "Excuse me, please."

Rule 10: **Place a comma between the day and year in a date.**

July 4, 1776

↑

Place a comma between the name of a day and date.

Saturday, June 29, 1996

Rule 11: **Place a comma between a town (village, city) and a state.**

Columbus, Ohio

↑

Place a comma between a city and a country.

London, England

↑

In a street address, place a comma after the street and after the city. Do not place a comma between the state and zip code. Do not place a comma between the house number and the street address.

They live at 2 Ridge Lane, Waynesville, NC 28786.

Do not place a comma after the street when addressing an envelope.

Rule 12: **Use a comma between two or more descriptive adjectives (describing words) _unless one is a color or number_.**

A tiny, playful kitten romped through the house.

↑

A tiny white kitten romped through the house.   (no comma)

Directions: Insert a comma where needed.

1.   She was born on August 3 1985.

2.   Does Joan live in Anaheim California?

3.   That reporter travels to Paris France.

4.   Smooth round balls were used for a game.

5.   His address is 1249 Cedar Drive Warrenton Missouri 63383.

6.   Beautiful unusual orchids were delivered on Friday November 20 1996.

Rule 1:   Use a colon in writing the time.

5:30 P. M.

Rule 2:   Use a colon to set off lists.

Food for picnic:
- hot dogs
- rolls
- marshmallows

The following are needed for first aid class: bandages, gauze, and tape.

Rule 3:   Use a colon after divisions of topics.

Class Rules:
At Your Seat: Keep your desk cleared.

Push in your chair when leaving.

Directions: Insert a colon where needed.

1.   Items needed for our camping trip
- tent
- lantern
- ice chests

2.   I have asked the following people to help Tate Val and Pedro

3.   Playground Rules

Rules for Slide   Do not go down on your stomach.
Wait until the person in front of you is out of the area.

4.   Lala ordered the following   napkins, a tablecloth, and place mats.

5.   Please bring the following items to the 7 00 art class   brushes, paints, and pads.

Question Mark (?):

Rule: **Use a question mark at the end of an interrogative sentence.** An interrogative sentence asks a question.

May I take your coat**?**

Exclamation Point (Mark) (!):

Rule 1: **Use an exclamation point after an exclamatory sentence.** An exclamatory sentence shows strong feeling.

We're just about finished**!**

Rule 2: **Use an exclamation point after a word or phrase that shows strong feeling.** A phrase is a group of words that does not have a subject and verb.

Yeah**!**   Hurrah**!** We're the champions!

🍓🍓🍓🍓🍓🍓🍓🍓🍓🍓🍓🍓🍓🍓🍓🍓🍓🍓🍓🍓🍓🍓🍓🍓🍓🍓🍓🍓🍓🍓🍓🍓🍓🍓🍓🍓

A. Directions: Write on the line provided.

1. Write a question you might ask someone in your family. _____

_____

2. Write a question you might ask a friend. _____

_____

B. Directions: Insert question marks or exclamation points where needed.

1. " We won " Jana exclaimed.

2. Do you know how to polish rocks

3. Yippee   I'm going up in a hot air balloon soon

4. How many grams are in an ounce

214

Rule 1: **Use a hyphen between fractions.**

one-half   two-thirds

Rule 2: **Use a hyphen between two digit word numbers between 21 and 99.**

twenty-one   fifty-eight

Rule 3: **Use a hyphen between a series of page numbers.**

I read pages 32-35 in my science book.

Rule 4: **Use a hyphen to combine some closely related words.**

forget-me-nots (flowers)   five-speed

Rule 5: **Use a hyphen when dividing a word of two or more syllables at the end of a line. <u>You must have at least two letters on the first line and three on the following line</u>.**

_____ bat-
ter _____ re-
maining _____

Directions: Insert hyphens where needed.

1. One third of the doughnuts had been eaten.

2. _____ During the summer, our fam

ily went to Washington, D. C., our

nation's capitol. We toured the Jef

ferson Memorial which honors one

of our nation's great men.

3. His uncle has a farm with thirty five dairy cows.

4. John's happy go lucky attitude makes him fun.

5. Kerry read from pages 77 109 to finish her book.

Rule 1: **Underline the name of ships, planes, and trains.**

The airplane, <u>Sky Queen</u>, is very fast.

Rule 2: **Underline the title of a book.**

My brother read the book <u>The Egg Tree</u>.

Rule 3: **Underline the title of a magazine.**

The woman was reading a copy of <u>Business Update</u>.

Rule 4: **Underline the title of a newspaper.**

His grandfather enjoys <u>The Western Journal</u>.

Rule 5: **Underline the title of a movie or television show.**

Have you seen the movie, <u>My Fair Lady</u>?
Their family usually watches <u>Kyla's Cooking Show</u> together.

NOTE: **If you are using a computer or a typewriter, a name or title that is usually underlined will be in italics.** *This sentence is in italic print.*

Their family watches*Kyla's Cooking Show* together.

Directions: Underline where needed.

1. Have you ever seen a picture of the ship, Lusitania?

2. His dad read him a children's book entitled Ali's School Bus.

3. Gone with the Wind is still her favorite movie.

4. Mother's favorite television show is Jeopardy.

5. Dad usually reads The Evening Sun (newspaper).

6. Tom Thumb was the first locomotive (train) in America.

Rule 1: **Place quotation marks around exactly what a person says.**

Mr. Brown said, "I bought a new camera today."
"Where did you buy it?" asked his wife.

A. **In a split quotation, place quotation marks around each part spoken.**

"Do you know," asked Sandra, "if the grocery store closes at ten o'clock?"

B. **In conversation, begin a new paragraph each time a different person speaks.**

Marty asked, "Why are party hats, horns, and streamers lying on the kitchen table?"
"We are having a surprise birthday party for Billy," said **Joyce** with a smile.
"Have you made a cake?" asked **Marty**.

Rule 2: **Place quotation marks around the titles of articles, short stories, short poems, songs, and chapters.**

"Working at Home"   (article)
"Abe Lincoln Grows Up"   (short story)
"Do You Fear the Force of the Wind?"   (poem)
"Go Down, Moses"   (song)
"Plants"   (chapter)

Place commas and periods inside quotation marks. I wrote a poem entitled "Me."

Directions: Insert needed quotation marks.

1. Miss Fenton wrote an article entitled Nuts and Bolts.

2. My science project is about magnets, said Krissy.

3. See the Trees is a poem by Carl Sandburg.

4. Robert asked, Why is the floor wet?

5. Have you read the story, Trademark, by Jessamyn West?

6. I think, said Ed, that I'd like a snack.

Name_____

Date_____

Directions: Insert needed punctuation.

period (.)   **exclamation point (!)**
apostrophe (')   **hyphen (-)**
comma (,)   **underlining (_)**
colon (:)   **quotation marks (" ")**
question mark (?)

1. Was Franks arm broken

2. They need the following drinks   lemonade punch and soda

3. Wow   Were state champions

4. Nate said   The line forms here

5. He moved to Seattle on Saturday July 5 1996

6. The ladies bathroom had been closed at 9 00 P M

7. Gail do you want a copy of Rising Tide magazine

8. Twenty eight students rode a bus to Orem Utah

9. She read a magazine article entitled A Choice for Change

10. Glendas favorite book is Indian Captive

11. No you cant eat in the living room

12. Mr Freed said   I must leave now

218

Name_____

Date_____

Directions: Insert needed punctuation.

period (.)	**exclamation point (!)**
apostrophe (')	**hyphen (-)**
comma (,)	**underlining (_)**
colon (:)	**quotation marks (" ")**
question mark (?)	

1. Dear Joanna

      It hasnt rained for several months here in our desert val

ley   However we believe that youll like life in Phoenix Arizona

See you soon
Annette

2. Please give this envelope to Sen R Ross

3. He didnt win the mens golf tournament

4. Three fourths of the entrants had won a ribbon

5. Things for camp
     - toothbrush
     - toothpaste

6. During the summer rain fell

7. Jill has read the poem entitled The Last of the Books

8. I   Water forms
      A   Oceans
      B   Gulfs and bays

9. Did Madelines dad buy that huge plastic barrel for trash

PUNCTUATION
Review

Directions: Insert needed punctuation.

period (.)   **exclamation point (!)**
apostrophe (')   **hyphen (-)**
comma (,)   **underlining (_)**
colon (:)   **quotation marks (" ")**
question mark (?)

1.   Jacys family reunion will be held on Sunday Aug 23

2.   Miss Bencze said We dont need the following glue paper or crayons

3.   Yeah   Our team has won another championship

4.   My brother and sister have read the book entitled What I Like About Toads

5.   We havent been to Atlantic City   said Mrs Lopez

6.   Forty two gifts had been placed on the brides table

7.   Adams John Q

8.   Is their new address 9987 W Cherry Drive Elmira OR   97404

9.   The three girls dad has given them a magazine subscription

10.   Dear Jemima
        We will meet you on Sat by the old mill at 8 30 A M
                                        Love
                                        Cousin Thang

11.   No those sweaters slacks and blouses arent for sale

A sentence expresses a complete thought. The subject of a sentence is **who** or **what** is being discussed in the sentence.

> **Example:** My hermit crab wakes at night.

We are talking about a crab. *Crab* is the subject of the sentence.

Sometimes, the sentence is about more than one thing.

> **Example:** His aunt and uncle camp.

We are talking about his aunt **and** uncle. *Aunt* and *uncle* are the subjects of the sentence. We call this a **compound subject**. Usually, we use ***and*** to join two words in a compound subject.

ฮ๛ฮ๛ฮ๛ฮ๛ฮ๛ฮ๛ฮ๛ฮ๛ฮ๛ฮ๛ฮ๛

Directions: Use ***and*** to join the subject of these sentences.

> **Example:** Lori washed a dog. Tate washed a dog.
>
> **Lori and Tate washed a dog.**

1. Tara made brownies. Her brother made brownies, too.

_____

_____

2. A hen ate grain. Little chicks ate grain, also.

_____

_____

3. An art fair will be held on Friday. A farmers' market will be held on Friday.

_____

_____

MY OWN NOTES

The subject of a sentence is **who** or **what** the sentence is "about."
Sometimes, a verb may change.

Example: Lee **packs** a snack. Tessa **packs** a snack, too.

When we talk about one (singular), we use a singular verb. Each person *packs* a snack. However, when we join *Lee* and *Tessa*, we have two items (plural) in the subject. The verb must agree with the plural subject. A plural verb in present time does **not** end in *s*. Therefore, Lee and Tessa **pack** a snack.

ༀ ༀ ༀ

A verb may change form with a compound subject.

Example: His bike **was** stolen. His skateboard **was** also stolen.

When we talk about one (singular), we use a singular verb *(was)*. When we are talking about **two or more** joined by *and*, we must use a verb that agrees.

Wrong: His bike and skateboard **was** stolen.

Right: His bike and skateboard **were** stolen.

ༀ ༀ ༀ ༀ ༀ ༀ ༀ ༀ ༀ ༀ

Directions: Use *and* to join the subjects of two sentences.

Example: My friend has ice skates. I have ice skates.

My friend and I have ice

skates.

1. Venus is a planet. Pluto is a planet.

_____

_____

2. His pug sleeps on his bed. His collie sleeps on his bed, too.

   _____

   _____

3. Miss Hill teaches at Jefferson Middle School. Mr. Lane teaches at Jefferson Middle School.

   _____

   _____

4. Their mother sings to them. Their grandmother sings to them, too.

   _____

   _____

5. Her boss talks on the telephone often. She talks on the telephone often, also.

   _____

   _____

6. Borax is a mineral. Jet is a mineral.

   _____

   _____

7. Jo skis every winter. Gary skis every winter.

   _____

   _____

The subject of a sentence is **who** or **what** the sentence is "about."
Sometimes, a verb may change.

Example: Their car **runs** well. Their truck **runs** well.

When we talk about one (singular), we use a singular verb. Each car *runs* well. However, when we join *car* and *truck*, we have two items (plural) in the subject. The verb must agree with the plural subject. A plural verb in present time does **not** end in *s*. Therefore, their car and truck **run** well.

ぅぅぅ

A verb may change form with a compound subject.

Example: Ken **has** a job. Amy **has** a job.

When we talk about one (singular), we use a singular verb *(has)*. When we are talking about **two or more** joined by **and**, we must use a verb that agrees.

　　Wrong: Ken and Amy **has** a job.

　　Right: Ken and Amy **have** a job.

ぅぅぅぅぅぅぅぅぅぅぅぅ

Directions: Use **and** to join the subjects of two sentences.

Example: His sister raises pigs.
　　　　　　　　His brother raises pigs.

__His sister and brother raise pigs.__

1.   Alvah likes to paint flowers on chairs.
　　His mother likes to paint flowers on chairs.

_____

_____

2. Barbie hands out programs at baseball games.
   Her father also hands out programs at baseball games.

   _____

   _____

3. My grandma is a greeter for a department store.
   He is a greeter for a department store, also.

   _____

   _____

4. Our friend buys Christmas gifts during the summer.
   Her husband buys Christmas gifts during the summer, too.

   _____

   _____

5. Chessa talks loudly.
   Randy talks loudly.
   Their older brother also talks loudly.

   _____

   _____

6. A striped pillow is lying on the wooden floor.
   A bright throw is lying on the wooden floor.

   _____

   _____

7. That electrician installs lights.
   The electrician's son installs lights.

   _____

   _____

MY OWN NOTES

Two items can be joined by a conjunction; the coordinating conjunctions are **and, or,** and **but**. Items joined do **not** have to be the subject of a sentence.

Examples: Please *read this paper* and *sign* at the bottom.

We do our homework *before* or *after* dinner.

The ushers for the play were *she and I*.

Nicky's bedspread is *bright pink* and *lacy*.

I'll take your *pennies* or *dimes*.

ঙ ঙ ঙ

Sometimes, <u>three or more items</u> are joined.

Example: A tractor, a plow, and a hay wagon are in that barn.

Place a comma after the items in a series that occur before *and*. Do not place a comma after **and/or** or after the *last item*.

Example: His mother bought a hammer, a saw, nails, and wood for the project.

ঙ ঙ ঙ ঙ ঙ ঙ ঙ ঙ ঙ ঙ ঙ

Directions: Join sentences.

Example: I like fresh fruit.
I like fruit cocktail.
I like dried fruit.

<u>**I like fresh fruit, fruit cocktail, and dried fruit.**</u>

1. Her uncle is tall.
   Her uncle is tan.
   Her uncle is muscular.

_____

_____

2. Linda will be a bridesmaid in their wedding.
   Mika will be a bridesmaid in their wedding.
   Lea will be a bridesmaid in their wedding.

   _____

   _____

3. That toddler scribbles on walls.
   That toddler scribbles on floors.
   That toddler also scribbles on furniture.

   _____

   _____

4. Peter works slowly.
   Peter works carefully.
   Peter works tirelessly.

   _____

   _____

5. The clerk smiled.
   The clerk handed the customer change.
   The clerk thanked him.

   _____

   _____

6. Visitors from Japan come to Hoover Dam.
   Visitors from India come to Hoover Dam.
   Visitors from Peru come to Hoover Dam.

   _____

   _____

Two items can be joined by a conjunction; the coordinating conjunctions are *and, or,* and *but*. Items joined do **not** have to be the subject of a sentence.

> **Examples:**   A *tartan* **and** a *skiff* are boats.
>
> The champion was *Kari* **or** her *sister*.
>
> Carlo collects *shells* **and** *marbles*.
>
> The four-year-old <u>frowned</u> **but** <u>didn't cry</u>.
>
> She seemed *quiet* **and** *shy*.

❧ ❧ ❧

Sometimes, <u>three or more items</u> are joined.

> **Example:**   A tractor, a plow, and a hay wagon are in that barn.

Place a comma after the items in a series that occur before *and*. Do not place a comma after *and/or* or after the *last item*.

> **Example:**   Gail bought sheets, pillowcases, and a blanket.

❧ ❧ ❧ ❧ ❧ ❧ ❧ ❧ ❧ ❧ ❧

Directions: Join sentences.

> **Example:**   Her tart is covered with strawberries.
> Her tart is covered with blueberries.
> Her tart is covered with raspberries.
>
> **<u>Her tart is covered with strawberries, blueberries,</u>**
> **<u>and raspberries.</u>**

1. The children are decorating birthday cupcakes with frosting.
    The children are decorating birthday cupcakes with coconut.
    The children are decorating birthday cupcakes with sprinkles.

    _____

    _____

2. Plastic shelves have been added to their closet.
   Plastic bins have been added to their closet.
   Plastic hooks have been added to their closet.

   _____

   _____

3. The baby waved his hands excitedly.
   The baby laughed.
   The baby jumped up and down.

   _____

   _____

4. A skater should use knee pads.
   A skater should use a mouth guard.
   A skater should use a helmet.

   _____

   _____

5. This gadget peels lemons.
   This gadget peels limes.
   This gadget peels oranges.

   _____

   _____

6. His apple pie turned out flaky.
   His apple pie turned out delicious.

   _____

   _____

MY OWN NOTES

An appositive is a word or phrase (group of words) that explains something in a sentence.

Example: Franco, ***my barber***, is from Italy.
                              appositive

An appositive is placed next to the word it explains.

Example: I like Fendi, ***her dog***.
                              appositive

An appositive is set off by commas.

Examples: Do you want to visit Newberg, a city in Oregon?

Their doctor, Dr. Hand, won a 5K race.

ക്ക ക്ക ക്ക ക്ക ക്ക ക്ക ക്ക ക്ക ക്ക ക്ക ക്ക

Directions: Place the appositive by the word it explains. Be sure to insert a comma or commas where needed.

Example: A puffin has a brightly colored bill.
                    A puffin is a bird.

___**A puffin**_____ **has a brightly colored bill.**___

___**A puffin,** *a bird*, **has a brightly colored bill.**___

1. Cassie is my older sister. Cassie loves to talk on the telephone.

___**Cassie**_____ **loves to talk on**___

___**the telephone.**___

2. Kari is my cousin's new baby. Kari weighs six pounds, nine ounces.

_____ **Kari** _____ **weighs six** _____

_____ **pounds, nine ounces.** _____

3. Hannah and Devi like to ride Chester. Chester is their horse.

_____ **Hannah and Devi like to ride Chester** _____

_____

4. Teiglach is good. Teiglach is a mixture of dough and honey.

_____ **Teiglach** _____

_____ **is good.** _____

5. His best friend visited a castle. His best friend's name is Robert Lee.

_____ **His best friend** _____ **visited a castle.** ____

6. A three-year-old is crying. Her name is Katie.

_____ **Katie** _____ **is crying.** _____

7. They spied a spatangoid. A spatangoid is a heart-shaped sea urchin.

_____ **They spied a spatangoid** _____

_____

8. My grandparents visited Zermatt. Zermatt is a town in Switzerland.

_____ **My grandparents visited Zermatt** _____

_____

Name________________________________ **Writing Sentences**

Date________________________________ **Appositives**

An appositive is a word or phrase (group of words) that explains something in a sentence.

Example: Coco, ***my canary***, is yellow.

appositive

An appositive is placed next to the word it explains.

Example: Have you read this book, ***a mystery***?

appositive

An appositive is set off by commas.

Examples: Hand me the ladle, that spoon with a long handle.

Abraham Lincoln, the 16th president, was tall.

Directions: Place the appositive by the word it explains. Be sure to insert a comma or commas where needed.

Example: We went to Sitka.
Sitka is a seaport in Alaska.

We went to Sitka________________________________

We went to Sitka, *a seaport in Alaska.*________________________________

1. His father loves to hike on weekends. His father is a manager.

His father__________________ **loves to hike on**

weekends.________________________________

2. Aegina is known for its beauty and clean air. Aegina is an island in Greece.

    __**Aegina**_____**is known for its**____

    __**beauty and clean air.**_____

3. Do you want to see Poppy? Poppy is my pet pig.

    __**Do you want to see Poppy**_____

    _____

4. The leaves of puha are used as vegetables in some lands. Puha is a plant.

    __**The leaves of puha**_____**are used as**____

    __**vegetables in some lands.**_____

5. Miss Lipos sold our home for us. Miss Lipos is our neighbor.

    __**Miss Lipos**_____**sold our home for us.**___

6. Bo is a kitten. Bo is Parker's favorite pet.

    __**Bo**_____**is Parker's favorite pet.**_____

7. I like honey. It is the only food that doesn't spoil.

    __**I like honey**_____

    _____

8. A dentist removed plaque from Andy's teeth. Plaque is a hard substance.

    __**A dentist removed plaque**_____

    __**from Andy's teeth.**_____

An appositive is a word or phrase (group of words) that explains something in a sentence.

      Example: Bruno, ***my dog***, is playful.

                          appositive

My dog explains who Bruno is.   Look at the sentence without *my dog*.

    Bruno is playful.

We have no idea who Bruno is.   Perhaps he is a cat, a ferret, or even a person. *My dog* explains who Bruno is.

An appositive is placed next to the word it explains.

      Example: Do you know Miss Logan, *my teacher*?

                                appositive

An appositive is set off by commas.

      Example: Brad, my best friend**,** is moving to New York.

           ৶৶৶৶৶৶৶৶৶৶৶৶

Directions: Using an appositive, combine these sentences.   Be sure to use commas where needed.

      Example: Peter is a police officer.
                     Peter is our son.

            Peter, our son, is a police officer.

1.   Mr. Sine is nice.
     Mr. Sine is the manager of a hardware store.

    _____

    _____

2. Newgate was a famous London prison.
   It was torn down in 1902.

   _____

   _____

3. Moody draws colorful cartoons.
   Moody is a high school art student.

   _____

   _____

4. My aunt and uncle live in Tampa.
   Tampa is a city in Florida.

   _____

   _____

5. They visited the Louvre.
   The Louvre is an art museum in Paris.

   _____

   _____

6. Their children are Pablo, Maria, and Anita.
   Their children will be visiting during the holidays.

   _____

   _____

7. They picked blackberries.
   Blackberries are fruit that grows on a bramble bush.

   _____

   _____

INDEX